Pentag

Anita Jackson

Hutchinson of London

Other titles in the Spirals series

by Anita Jackson

A Game of Life or Death
The Actor
The Austin Seven
The Ear
Bennet Manor
Dreams

Hutchinson & Co (Publishers) Ltd
3 Fitzroy Square, London W1P 6JD

London Melbourne Sydney Auckland
Wellington Johannesburg and agencies
throughout the world
First published 1977
Set in Stymie medium
© Anita Jackson 1977
Printed in Great Britain at The Anchor Press
and bound by Wm Brendon & Son Ltd both of
Tiptree, Essex

ISBN 0 09 131011 3

1

The sky was a deep rich blue. The sea was as smooth
as glass. Miles and miles of shining blue-green water.
Ken Wilson sat with his head propped up on his
hands and looked at it. This was the life. Sun, sea and
fresh air. No one about. Just a few sea gulls drifting
about in the sky and one or two crabs crossing the
yellow sand.

Ken had just been for a swim and his red trunks were
still wet. With a lazy sweep of his hand he picked
up some sand and let it drop on his legs. It ran over
his sun-tanned skin. 'I don't like these legs,' thought
Ken as he peered down at them. 'Slim legs are OK
but these are thin. Skinny. Not my cup of tea at all.'
He looked at the feet on the end of his thin legs and
shook his head. 'Too big by a long way. I hope I get
a size nine next time. And no corns. These feet give
me hell if I walk a few miles. It's like stepping on
pins.'

Crossly Ken dug his heels into the sand. He was
getting fed up with this body. He had never felt at
home in it. Never liked it. Not even when he saw it
for the first time ten weeks ago. He had stood looking
in the mirror with Doctor ZB4 beside him and said,

'It's fine. Very good.' But he didn't mean it. He just said it so that he wouldn't hurt the doctor's feelings. Well, ZB4 was a nice old chap. He'd put a lot of work into this body and it was a very neat job. Trim. Well made. Not a scar to be seen.

Ken didn't like the look of it but that was too bad. He wasn't paid to like it. Just to put up with it and use it for a few weeks. He was a PENTAG spy so it was no good being fussy about his looks. Every time they sent him to do a job they gave him a new body. 'The right body for the job.' That's what Doctor ZB4 always said and he knew what he was talking about. He had been a PENTAG re-fit doctor for ten years. 'If you need hands with a grip like steel or legs that can run a mile in 40 seconds, I'll give them to you,' said ZB4. 'When I've worked on a body it does the job. It won't let you down.'

Well, that was true. This body had done its job. Ken had spent six weeks near the North Pole. Six freezing weeks with ice and snow all round him. A team of Americans were working in a lab 100 feet under the ice cap. It was all very hush hush but PENTAG got wind of it and wanted to know what they were up to. There was one way to find out — slip a spy into the team. Ken was picked for the job. And a rotten job it was too. When the rest of the team were snug

4

in their sleeping bags he had to creep into the lab.
The place was as cold as an ice box. Most of the time
Ken felt more like an ice cube than a man. Just to
think about it made him shudder.

Still Ken had to admit that this body had stood up to
it. Bitter cold. Lack of sleep. This body had faced it
all. Now the job was done and Ken was here at a
PENTAG hide-out. He was alone and the nearest
town was fifty miles away. But that didn't bother him.
He was having a rest by the sea with nothing to do
all day but swim and sleep and laze about on the
sand.

The sun was creeping up in the sky. It was almost
mid-day. Too hot to lie in the sun. Ken closed one eye
and peered at the tip of his nose. It was red. 'Hell,
I'm getting burnt,' he thought. 'I'd better go back to
the villa.' He sat up quickly, then he smiled to
himself. There was no need to hurry. It didn't matter
if this body got a bit burnt. He would be going in for
a re-fit any day now. Doctor ZB4 would soon fix his
nose.

Yes, any day now. Maybe tomorrow. Maybe the
next day. The PENTAG net would pull him in. He
would get a little red card with his number on it and
he would be off to Unit 5 for a re-fit. After that he

would have a new job to do. Ken was ready to go.
Keen to get started. Some men drive fast cars. It
gives them a kick. But for Ken it was PENTAG
that put the fizz into life. The thought of a new job
went to his head like wine.

With shining eyes Ken gazed out to sea. A sea gull
swept down from the sky and landed on the water.
It bobbed up and down like a cork. Ken was still
looking at it when a sudden chill came over him. A
shiver ran up his spine. For a second he didn't know
why. Then it came to him in a flash. *He was not alone.*
'Someone is looking at me,' he thought. 'I can feel
it. There is someone behind me. Someone staring at
my back.'

Slowly Ken turned his head. His eyes moved from
sea to sand. Nothing. No one there. He turned his
neck a bit more. Behind him there was a strip of flat
sand, then some trees. In the heat the air seemed to
shimmer. Far away by the trees something moved. A
man. There *was* someone there. With a jerk Ken
spun all the way round. He felt for his gun but it was
a few feet away on the sand. Quickly he flung himself
down and grabbed it. When he looked up the man
had gone.

Flat on his belly, Ken waited. Was someone going

to take a shot at him? Was someone hiding in the trees? Time ticked by. Nothing happened. The waves lapped on the sand and up in the sky a sea gull gave a cry. That was all. Very slowly Ken stood up. He felt a bit of a fool standing there all alone with the gun in his hand. Maybe he had made a mistake. Maybe his eyes were playing tricks on him. He tried to get a grip on himself but it wasn't easy. Just a few days ago the same thing had happened. 'I'm jumpy,' thought Ken. 'I'm going for my gun every time I see a shadow. I must pull myself together.'

Ken shook the sand out of his vest and put it on. He picked up his stuff. His air bed. His sun glasses. His empty beer can. Then he walked back to the villa. Under his feet the sand was hot and gritty. It dug into his corns. Ken kept his hand on his gun and every now and then he looked behind him. He couldn't see anyone but it was better to be safe than sorry. A spy is always at risk. He can never relax.

As Ken went up the steps to the villa he looked back at the trees. He still had that feeling. Hidden eyes. Someone staring at him. He couldn't shake it off. Maybe there was someone after him. Maybe someone had followed him to this lonely PENTAG hideout. If that was so . . . well, things could get tricky.

2

As soon as Ken was indoors he made himself a stiff drink and sat down. 'Take it easy,' he thought. 'It's no good getting in a flap.' Near him on the wall was a push button. Ken flicked it with his toe and a fan buzzed into life. Cool air began to drift round the room. That felt better. Ken picked up a book and began to read. The room was very still. The fan hummed and a clock ticked softly. That was all. It's a very lonely sound, the ticking of a clock. But it didn't bother Ken. He was used to being alone.

Soon Ken put the book aside. He was going to have a shower. That's what he needed. Cool jets of water playing on his skin. Wash the sand and salt off his body. He began to walk towards the bathroom but at his bedroom door he stopped. He saw something. There was a card on the bed. A little red card. Ken ran and picked it up. It had his number on the top. *This was it.* PENTAG was calling him in for a refit.

Ken jumped onto the bed and hopped up and down like a kid. At last. This was it. He would soon have a new body. About time too. Out of the corner of his eye he saw himself in the mirror. Hopping up and down like a yo-yo. He grinned and sat down on the bed. 'OK,' he said to his legs. 'This is the end of the line for you. You've had it. Doctor ZB4 can dump you in the dustbin or give you to some poor out-of-luck spy. I won't miss you. I'll be glad to see the back of you.'

Still grinning Ken got his case and began to pack. He had to be ready to go when the pick-up team called for him. There was no need to worry about the man by the trees. It must have been someone from PENTAG bringing the red card. If not . . . well, it didn't matter now. He would soon be out of this place. Soon be safe inside another body. No one can follow you if they don't know what you look like.

Ken finished sorting out his socks and pants. Then he got his jackets and began to pack them. It was odd to think that he wouldn't use these things again. Sad in a way. All these socks and jumpers and shoes. They wouldn't fit the next body. He would hand them in at Unit 5 and PENTAG would kit him out with new stuff. Every bit of it new. Even the toothbrush.

There was just one thing that Ken would keep. A very small thing. He picked it up from the bedside table and put it into his case. It was a photo. An old photo. The paper was a bit bent and grubby but a face smiled up at Ken. His own face. Ken Wilson. This was how he looked before he joined PENTAG. Young. Good looking. Black hair and blue eyes. A small neat nose. Yes, it was a nice face. Ken smiled back at the photo then he snapped the case shut.

A soft humming filled the air and Ken went to the window. Was the pick-up team here so soon? Yes, he could see the plane. It was still high in the sky but getting closer all the time. Like a big silver bird it seemed to hover in mid-air. Then it dropped slowly and came to rest on the sand. These PENTAG planes didn't need a runway. They could rip across the sky as fast as a shooting star and then come down spot on target. It always looked so easy.

Now two men got out of the plane and began to plod across the sand to the villa. Ken knew what would happen next. He had done this many times before. The drill was always the same. He would be given a shot in the arm and soon he would be out cold. Then the pick-up team would put him into the plane. When he woke up he would be at Unit 5. Where was Unit 5? Was it in America or England? In China or India? Ken didn't know but it didn't bother him. He could see why it had to be like this. If he knew where the place was he might talk about it. He could be *made* to talk. This way was best.

Feet came thudding up the steps. They were here. It was time to go. Ken had a last look round the room. Had he packed all his stuff? Was his photo in the case? Yes, he was ready. The door gave a loud click and opened wide. Two men stepped in. Both were dressed in the PENTAG outfit and their faces were hidden by PENTAG masks. One lifted his hand in greeting but there was no time to chat. The pick-up drill was always like this.

About ten minutes later the plane rose slowly into the air. Ken was inside it lying on a padded bunk. He was in such a deep sleep that he seemed as lifeless as a log of wood. The trip to Unit 5 had begun.

3

'H12. H12, are you awake? It's supper time, H12.'

Someone was calling Ken's number. He opened his eyes and sat up quickly. He was in a little white room with four beds. Two were empty but a hump under the blankets showed that someone was in the bed next to his. The lights were full on but Ken could tell that it was dark outside. This was the rest room at Unit 5. Ken must have been asleep for hours.

A girl holding a tray of drinks stood by his bed. Her yellow hair made a frame of curls round the PENTAG mask. Ken grinned at her and said, 'What's for supper? I feel like a nice pork chop or maybe ham and eggs.' The girl let her lips part in a smile. 'Now, H12,' she said. 'Stop making fun of me. You know you are having a re-fit tomorrow so you can't have solid food. Here's your supper.'

Ken took the glass she held out and drank the stuff in one gulp. He made a face. 'I'll never get used to this muck,' he said. 'One of these days I'll show you how to mix a good drink.' The girl took the empty glass and walked to the door. With his eyes Ken followed her long legs and slim hips. 'Pretty girl,' he thought.

'A bit like Sandy — or was her name Susan?' He couldn't quite remember. Anyway it didn't matter. Just a girl he had met when he was on a tricky job. It was odd that he could remember her at all. A re-fit made you forget things. It wiped out the past. That was a good thing for a spy. It was safe.

A grunt came from the next bed and the heap of blankets moved. A young man pushed his head out and blinked in the bright light. He stared at Ken, then at the room. 'Where am I?' he said. 'Is this Unit 5?' Ken nodded. This chap must be new to the job. You could always tell. 'It's good to see your face,' said the young man. 'All these people with masks on . . . it gives me the creeps.'
'You get used to it,' said Ken. 'If you see a face in Unit 5, it's a face that won't be around for long. I'm getting rid of mine tomorrow.' The young man turned pale. 'So am I,' he said. 'I'm not looking forward to it. Not at all. I've never done this before.' His hand gripped the blanket and he said, 'I don't know if I'm up to it. I'm thinking of calling it off.'

'We all get cold feet,' said Ken. 'Don't worry. PENTAG will look after you. You will be OK when the first re-fit is over. It will take you a few days to get used to your new body. Then you'll be fine.' The young man looked down at himself. Then he said

13

softly, 'The new body . . . how will it feel? You must know. Tell me what it feels like.'

Ken gave a shrug. 'It's never the same so I can't really tell you. You will find that the new body has its own habits. Its own way of doing things. If you kept your old habits you could give yourself away. You know what I mean. You can get to know a man's footsteps or his way of tapping on a door. We don't run that risk. No one can pick us out.' The young man looked blank. He didn't seem to be taking it in. Ken bent over and slapped him on the back. 'You are going to be a *spy*, not a milkman,' he said. 'After every job you will be a marked man. You'll be glad to get into a new body.'

The young man nodded. 'Yes, I know. But Doctor ZB4 told me that the body would fit the job. He said he might give me a stammer to make me seem very shy. I don't fancy that.' Ken grinned and stuck one of his feet in the air. 'Look at that,' he said. 'Corns. A prize set of corns. But there's no need to get upset. You don't keep anything for long. As soon as you get the feel of a body it's time to trade it in. You move on. Don't let the little snags put you off. With PENTAG you really live. You do new things. You feel new things. You can pack a hundred lives into one lifetime.'

14

Suddenly the light grew dim. 'Time to sleep now,'
said Ken. 'Don't worry about tomorrow. You'll be OK
with ZB4. He's good. I should know. He's done a lot
of work on me.' Ken pushed his pillow into shape and
soon he was asleep. The young man was still awake.
For a long time he gazed up into the darkness.

4

The next day Ken had his re-fit. After that he lay in a misty dream land for a week. Not awake but not quite asleep. Sometimes he could hear things but the sound was dull and far away. Under his closed eyelids lights seemed to shine, then fade. Shadows seemed to flit about. Nothing was clear. Nothing had any shape.

As he lay there his new body had time to heal. It didn't take long. The PENTAG doctors knew how to speed things up. They had it off to a fine art. Just a week after the re-fit Ken was OK again. His eyes opened wide and suddenly the things around him snapped into shape. There was the wall. There was the end of his bed. And there was Doctor ZB4 standing beside him. The doctor was smiling under his PENTAG mask so the re-fit must have gone well.

 Glad to see you, Doc,' said Ken. 'How do I look?' Then he added, 'Well, now I've heard myself speak. Not bad at all. I sound fine. How about the rest of me?' ZB4 looked shy, almost coy. Then he said, 'I've done a very good job. I shouldn't say so myself but this body is one of my best bits of work. Come and take a look in the mirror.' Most of ZB4's face was hidden by his mask but the bit that Ken could see was pink with pride.

Ken swung his legs out of bed and felt the floor with his new feet. He tested them. Pressed down on his heels. Made his toes fan out. 'I'll give you ten out of ten for the feet, Doc,' he said. 'Not too big. Not too small. No corns. Feet fit for a king.' Slowly he stood up and began to walk to the big mirror at the end of the room. His body moved in a smooth, free way. 'Good,' thought Ken. 'This body is fit. Strong.' In a few seconds he was looking at himself in the glass. Gazing at the new Ken Wilson.

For a long time he didn't speak. Then with a smile that showed his gleaming white teeth he said, 'What's going on, Doc? Am I a spy or a film star? It's OK to be good looking but haven't you overdone it? Haven't you gone a bit too far?' He looked again at the fine tall body. The well shaped head. The thick brown hair. The face with its dazzling smile. 'Come on, Doc,' he said. 'What's this body for? I hope I haven't got to play the part of a male pin-up in my next job. That's not my line at all. I would feel a fool.'

ZB4 shook his head. 'No, no,' he said. 'Don't worry, H12. You won't have to do anything like that. Your job will be to find out about some gas. Deadly stuff.

17

One drop of it set free in the air will wipe out a town. The gas is man-made and we want to know how to make it. This body will help you. I'll tell you how. In this job you will need to get on with women. They don't make the gas but they do most of the paper work in the place. If they like you and trust you the job will be easy. So you see how it is. You must use your good looks. Use your charm.'

Ken tested his smile again. 'I think I'm going to enjoy this job. But I don't like the sound of that gas. I hope I've got lungs that will stand up to it.' 'No need for that,' said ZB4. 'You won't have to go near it. All the facts we need are kept in a safe. Open the safe and get a copy. That's all there is to it. Now come on, H12. We mustn't waste time. There's a lot to do before you go.'

Ken slipped a mask over his new face and tugged it into place. Then ZB4 handed Ken his job card. It wasn't much to look at. Just a sheet of stiff white paper with a lot of little holes punched in it. This would tell Ken all he needed to know about his next job. Ken tucked it under his arm and walked briskly to room 20. Here he would find out what the card said.

By now Ken had almost forgotten his last job. Things that happened six weeks ago were dim in his mind.

Wiped out by his re-fit. Now he had things to learn.
He went into Room 20 and sat down in the learning
chair. The first time he did this it was a bit like going
to the dentist. But now it didn't bother him. He fed
his job card into a slot and pressed his hands onto
the soft pads at the side of the chair. Metal bands
clicked over to hold him in place. Then a sort of hood
came down over his head.

Two hours later Ken got out of the chair. Now he
knew all about his new job, and he knew all about
David West. That was his new name. For the next few
weeks he would be David West. Good looking Dave.
The man with the dazzling smile.

5

A week had gone by and Unit 5 was miles away.
Ken was in a dry, dusty part of America. The spot
wasn't marked on any map. In this lonely place there
was a town. An odd sort of town that looked like a
cross between an airport and an army camp. It had
wide roads, tall blocks of flats, lots of huts and sheds
and a runway for planes. Here the deadly gas was
being made.

It wasn't the sort of place you would want to visit. If
you did happen to go there it wasn't easy to get in.
There were high walls all round it and men with guns
stood at the gates. No one could go in or out without
a pass.

Ken was now inside these walls. He was living there.
Working there. This was a big outfit and hundreds of
people were needed to keep it running. Ken had
been taken on to work in the pay room. He had a desk
with his name, David West, on it and he lived in a flat
just inside the main gate. A snug little place. Only a
step away from the block he worked in. Very handy.

Ken had done some odd things in his time as a spy.
He had worked deep under the sea. Been down a

gold mine. Taken a trip to the North Pole. Now he had to sit at a desk and get on with a pile of paper work. Most of the time he was dealing with pay slips. Adding up numbers. It was so dull that he could almost forget he was a spy.

But when he looked out of the window it all came back to him. The pay room was on the tenth floor of a tall block. If Ken looked down he could see trucks going out of the main gate and men with guns. He could see the tall shed where the gas was made. That made him think about his real job. His job for PENTAG.

He had to find out about that gas. Get the facts out of the safe. But it wasn't going to be easy. The safe was in the basement. Deep in the ground under the block that Ken worked in. He was sitting right on top of it. But how could he get down there without being seen? It was so near yet so far away.

For the time being Ken did his job in the pay room and kept his nose clean. He worked with a lot of old ladies and he played the part of the new boy. Getting them to show him around. Getting them to tell him how the place ticked. ZB4's body was doing its job. No one knew there was a spy behind the smiling face of Dave West.

There was one thing that Ken needed. A set of keys.
Most of the doors in this place were locked. As soon
as he got hold of some keys he could make a move.
Just one person in the pay room had keys. Ken's boss.
The best looking boss he'd ever worked for. Pam
Liston. She was young and clever and she was pretty.
A real doll. Ken set out to charm her. Every time he
saw her he gave her a dazzling smile. 'You may not
know it , young lady,' he thought, 'but I'm going to
play a big part in your love life for the next few
weeks.'

6

Work was over for the day. Ken was in his flat having a bath. Hot water lapped over his chest and little drops from his wet hair ran down his face. One foot was peeping out of the water and every now and then the cold tap dripped on it. Ken didn't bother to move. He lay back lazy and happy like a cat by a fire. It was almost time to get out of the bath and get dressed. Soon Pam Liston would be tapping on his door.

Yes, he was getting on well with Pam. At first she didn't seem to think much of his dazzling Dave West smile but then he got chatting to her. That did the trick. A few days later he kissed her. It was in the lift. On the way up to the pay room. A soft sweet kiss.

From then on Ken had been meeting her every night. Sometimes at her flat. Sometimes at his. Now she liked him. Trusted him. And that was what Ken had been waiting for. Pam was the pay room boss. She often stayed late at work. One night he would stay there with her. When the rest of the staff had gone he would take her keys. Go down to the safe. 'Yes, Pam's a nice girl,' thought Ken. 'She'll be a big help to me. I must hurry up and get out of this bath. She'll be here soon.'

He grabbed for the soap and it slipped into the bath with a plop. Ken felt for it in the water with his left hand. That was the one thing he didn't like about this body. He was left handed. Still it wasn't too bad. Not like having corns. Ken found the soap and pulled the plug out. Soon he was in the bedroom getting dressed.

'Now let's see,' he said to himself. 'What shall I put on? That blue silk shirt will do.' He slipped it on and went to the mirror to fix his tie. 'Just look at me,' he thought. 'A silk shirt and a gold tie pin. What a flashy dresser I am.' All his kit was like this. Smart and a bit flashy.

Ken's photo was propped up on the table. The old photo of himself. The paper face was smiling at him. 'You needn't smile,' Ken said to the photo. 'This outfit would look a bit silly on you but it looks OK on me. I've got the body for it.'

He was just going to dab some after-shave on his chin when a shadow moved across the window. 'There's someone outside,' thought Ken. 'Someone was looking in on me.' He dropped the after-shave and dashed across to the window. Quickly he flung it open — then he had to smile. No one could stand outside this window. It was about 20 feet above the ground. 'I'm getting jumpy again,' thought Ken. 'I must keep cool. That's rule number one in the spy game. If I forget it I won't live long.'

A soft tap at the door made him pull himself together. It was Pam. She was looking very pretty in a long green dress. 'I'm sorry I'm a bit late, Dave,' she said. 'I had to stay behind at work. There's a lot to do just now.' Ken smiled and said, 'That's what you get for being the boss. But don't worry. I don't mind waiting. If you like I'll stay at work tomorrow and wait for you. We can go home together. How about that?'

He said it smoothly as if it didn't matter at all. As if it had just crossed his mind. Pam thought for a bit. She knew it was against the rules. Ken waited with a smile fixed on his face. Would she say no? Would she mess up his plan? At last Pam nodded. 'Yes,' she said. 'I'd like that. I hate being there on my own. It seems so big and empty when the others have gone home.'

So it was fixed. The job was set up. Tomorrow was the big night. As soon as Ken had done the job he would slip away. Go back to PENTAG. In a way he was sorry. He would miss Pam. She was easy to get on with. Easy to talk to. In the last few weeks he had grown close to her. It was a pity to think that they would never be together like this again. Ken put his arms around her and kissed her soft lips.

The moon was shining high in the sky when Ken walked Pam back to her flat. They went slowly. Along the moonlit street. Past two look-out men standing in the shadows. 'This place is like a prison,' thought Ken. 'Pam doesn't belong here. I wish . . .'

He looked at her face resting on his arm. Felt her soft hair against his cheek. Suddenly it was as if the moon had cast a spell on him. Pam's face in the pale net of moonbeams was the most lovely face he had ever seen. Very softly she said his name, 'Dave.' That broke the spell. He was a PENTAG spy H12 and he had a job to do. It was no good letting his feelings get in the way.

Quickly he said goodnight and went back along the dim moonlit road. His plans were clear now. He knew what he would do. Tomorrow night he would go down the lift shaft. Not *in* the lift. No, he would get into the deep well that the lift moved in. That way he could get into the basement without being seen. With any luck it would be easy to find the safe. 'Right,' thought Ken. 'I must get to bed now. I need to be on top form tomorrow.'

But Ken didn't sleep well. Something happened that upset him. When he got back to his flat he found the door open. Nothing was missing but his photo was lying face down on the floor. 'It's easy to see what happened,' Ken said to himself. 'I was talking to Pam and I forgot to shut the door. A gust of wind blew in.' All the same he wasn't happy about it. He had the feeling that someone had been here. That someone had been in this room.

'It's just as well that I'll soon be away from this place,' thought Ken.

7

The next day went by slowly. There was a pile of paper work on Ken's desk but he kept looking out of the window. Looking at the ground far below. He was thinking about the safe in the basement. Waiting for the day to end. The hours dragged by and at last it began to get dark. 'Not long now,' thought Ken.

Soon the old lady next to him put her pens away and began to tidy her desk. It was time to go. All round Ken people stood up and put their coats on. In other rooms up and down the block people were getting ready to go. There was loud chatter and the clatter of feet. Then a hush fell. Ken was alone in the pay room.

He sat at his desk for a bit. Then he walked slowly across the room to Pam's door. She had her own little den next to the pay room. With a dazzling smile he said, 'How is it going, Boss?' Pam looked a bit glum. 'Not very well, Dave,' she said. 'I'll be here for hours. If you don't want to wait just tell me. The place is locked up now but I can let you out.'

'Don't worry about me,' said Ken. 'I'll go back into the pay room. I've got plenty of work to get on with.' He smiled and backed out of the room. As the door shut behind him the smile died on his lips. His face became a mask of sadness. In his hand he was holding Pam's keys. They had been lying on her desk. 'Forgive me, Pam,' he thought. 'I had to take them.'

Quickly Ken ran to his desk and got the small flat case he had hidden there. His gun was in it and the tools he needed to do the job. Then he slipped out of the pay room and set off towards the lift.

By day this place was full of life but now it was dark and empty. A few dim lights lit the long passage outside the pay room. As Ken ran along it his footsteps seemed loud. He kept running until a door blocked his way. Now for the keys. He tried them one by one and soon the big metal door swung open.

Now he was in darkness. Going slowly. Feeling his way. On into the gloom. Then another door. Where was the lock? Yes, he could feel it. Now which key? This one? Or this one? No. He tried them all again. This time he found it and the door opened smoothly.

Now there was some light. A dim yellow light glowing in the wall. Not much to see by but better than nothing. Here was the lift. He had made it to the lift. So far so good. Now was his plan going to work? He rubbed the little window in the lift door and peered in. He could see the black, empty shaft. Good. The lift itself was out of the way. He just had to open this door and step into the dark pit.

Ken took a few tools from his PENTAG case. This had to be a clean job. Nothing broken. Nothing smashed. Nothing left behind to give him away. With speed and skill he worked on the lift door. Soon it began to slide back. There was a gap. Very small. Getting wider. There. That would do. Ken bent down to pick up his tools then he heard something. Footsteps. One of the look-out men was coming this way.

Ken grabbed his little case and ran a few steps down the passage. Where could he hide? Nowhere. He would have to stand in the shadows. Hope that the look-out didn't see him. Quickly he pressed himself to the wall. The footsteps came nearer. Slow heavy footsteps. The man must be beside the lift now. Would he see that the door was open? 'He *must* see,' thought Ken. But no. He didn't see.

Now the beam of his flashlight was moving along the floor. Coming nearer. Ken crushed himself to the wall. Pulling himself in. Making his body flat. His toes were bunched up inside his shoes. Trying to pull back from the spot of light. 'Now he'll see me,' thought Ken but suddenly the look-out stopped. His light flashed over one wall. Then he turned and began to go back. He had seen nothing. His slow, heavy footsteps grew dull and faded away.

Ken wiped his wet face with his hand. Then he ran back to the lift. There was no time to waste. The man might come back. Quickly Ken fitted a soft rubber cap on his head. A small light was fixed to it. This way Ken could see what he was doing and keep both hands free. His little case was soon clipped to his belt and he was ready. Now for it. Into the lift shaft.

He put his head into the narrow gap and looked down. It was like looking into a deep well. No snug little lift to step into. Just a deep empty pit. Brick walls going down, down into darkness. Grimly Ken reached out for the thick cord that ran all the way down the shaft. 'Will it snap?' he thought. Then he smiled at himself. How silly, if this cord could pull the lift up and down it wasn't going to snap when one man slid down it.

He jumped at the metal cord. Grabbed it. Locked his arms and legs round it. Then he began to let himself down. 'Slowly now. Slowly,' he told himself. 'I mustn't lose my grip. If I fall I've had it.' Ken kept moving for

about ten minutes. Then he looked down. He must
be almost there. No. All he could see was a deep
dark pit and blackness. Was his body going to stand
up to this? His arms were going dead. Ken rested for
a bit, hanging in mid-air. Then he went on down.

It was OK. ZB4's body did its job. Just as Ken's hands
began to slip, he got to the bottom. He let go of the
cord and dropped to the ground with a thud.

8

Ken had made it. He was down at the bottom of the
lift shaft. The safe couldn't be far away but first Ken
had to get out of this black pit. He turned his head
and the light from his cap moved round the brick
walls. Round to the door. With a sinking feeling he
looked at it. This door was made to stop people like
Ken. It wouldn't be easy to get past it. He had tools
that would cut it open but that would take hours.
Anyway the door would end up in a mess. A real
give-away. No, there must be a better way out.

Ken spotted something on the wall just above his
head. He lifted his hand to feel it. It was cold. Made
of metal. He flashed the beam of his light to see
better. It was a wire cover fitted over a hole. Ken
gave a tug. The cover dropped to the ground with a
clang. Then Ken peered into the round hole. He knew
what it was. The end of an air pipe. There must be a
network of them feeding air to all the rooms in the
basement.

What luck. It was a ready made exit. Better than
that. It was a way to the safe. A cold, narrow way but
that didn't matter. If he crept along the inside of this
pipe he would find the room he was looking for. No

risk of running into any spy traps. This way he would by-pass them all.

Quickly he pulled himself into the pipe and felt the cold metal close round his body. There was just about room to move. Like a snake he crept along. Flat on his belly. There was no going back now. He couldn't turn round even if he wanted to.

The pipe went upwards for a bit then it dipped down. Ken dragged himself along as fast as he could. He came to a bend and the pipe got thinner. It was such a close fit that it was like a metal skin round his body. Ken felt a stab of fear. If he got stuck no one would ever find him. He would die inside this dark narrow pipe.

There was something just ahead. Two tiny spots of light in the darkness. Eyes. It was a rat with small glinting eyes. Ken froze. The rat stared at him. He could see its long yellow teeth. Then it came slowly towards him. It sniffed his face and he lay still. Cold as ice. Not daring to blink his eyes. He felt its soft fur on his cheek, then suddenly it turned and ran away down the pipe.

Ken licked his dry lips and moved on at top speed. Soon he came to a way out. The pipe got wider and there was a wire cover like the one in the lift shaft. Ken pushed it away and put his head out of the hole. He was looking down into a big room. The light from his cap shone on the floor. On the walls. Then he saw a safe at one end of the room. This was it. Thank God for that. He had found it.

In no time at all Ken was at work. This bit of the job was easy. He had all the things he needed in his little black case. Five minutes later the safe was open and Ken was holding a pile of papers. He ran his eye over the top page. It didn't mean much to him. Just rows and rows of numbers. Still, this was what PENTAG wanted. These numbers would tell them how to make the gas. Quickly Ken took a photo of each one. Then he stacked them neatly and put them back in the safe. No one would know that he had been here. Nothing was missing. Nothing out of place. If he could get back to the pay room the job would be finished.

Would he get away with it? Ken was hopeful. It hadn't been too bad after all, and he had been quick. He knew the way now so he could speed up on the way back. With any luck it would all be OK. Ken packed his stuff in his case. Then he fixed it to his belt. 'Right,' he thought. 'Back to the pay room. If Pam thinks I've been there all the time I'm in the clear. I must hurry.'

9

Very soon Ken was out of the pipe and back at the bottom of the lift shaft. He was feeling fine. Ready for the long slog up the rope. He took a last look round at the brick walls and the anti-spy door. Now he could smile at that door. It hadn't stopped him. He moved his cap so that the light shone upwards. Then he set off.

It was hard going. There was a bit of oil on the metal cord. It didn't matter on the way down but now he kept slipping back. Ken put some cloth round his hands and that helped. He could get a better grip. He pulled himself up as fast as he could. Time was ticking by. He had to hurry.

Soon he was panting and his arms were stiff. He tried to work out how far he had come. There was a door on each floor of the block. How many had he passed? Five. Maybe six. There was still a long way to go. The pay room was on the tenth floor. Ken gritted his teeth and speeded up. He passed two more doors. Then he rested hanging on the rope. 'Hell,' he thought, 'I'll never do it. ZB4 should have made me into an ape, not a man.' He grinned at the thought and pressed on.

In fact he was doing well. Going slowly. Slipping a bit now and then. But moving up all the time. Ken tipped his head back and the light from his cap swayed up the brick walls. Up the gloomy shaft. Up to another door. Ken rushed towards it. Was it this? No, it was shut fast. He couldn't get out here. Well, it must be the next one. Not far to go now.

Suddenly the rope in Ken's hands moved. It gave a shudder. He almost lost his grip. There was a sound above him. A loud rumbling. Sick with shock he looked up. The lift was coming down. It couldn't be. But it *was*. It was coming down the shaft. Ken was right in its path. What could he do?

There was no time to think. The lift was moving quickly. Getting nearer. Big and heavy it loomed over the small shape of the man. It filled the lift shaft. No space at the side for Ken to creep into. In panic he began to let himself down the rope. Trying to get away from the lift. Trying to keep ahead. It followed him down. Smooth and steady it moved after him. As he looked up he felt small and helpless. Like an ant under a man's foot. The lift was going to crush him to death.

'Maybe it will stop,' thought Ken. 'Maybe it isn't going all the way down.' But the lift kept moving. Ken slid down the rope at a dizzy speed. The walls were a blur. The doors flashed past him. Then he let go. He was down at the bottom of the shaft. 'Quick,' he thought. 'into the air pipe.'

But it was too late. The lift was just above him. It covered the pipe. It brushed the top of his head. In panic he beat on the door. The useless locked door. Then he fell to the floor. He was trapped. Nothing could save him now. With wide eyes he looked at the lift. It was almost down. Horror filled him. It was pressing on his body. Pressing on his face. He closed his eyes. One second seemed to last for ever. Time stood still. 'Am I dead yet? Am I dead?' he thought.

But when he opened his eyes he was alive. The lift had stopped. For a second it stayed there. Resting on his body. Resting on his skull like a hammer on an egg shell. Then it gave a jolt and began to go up. Ken gave a cry and rolled over. His shaking body rolled right out of the lift shaft. The door was open. Wide open. And Pam was standing there. She had saved his life.

Her face was pale and sad as she helped him to his feet. 'So you are a spy,' she said. 'I think I knew it all along. Don't speak. I don't want to hear any more lies. Just come with me.' Ken looked at her blankly.

'Hurry,' she said. 'A look-out man was on his way down in the lift. I pressed the cut out button and sent him up again. He'll be back soon. If he finds you here he'll shoot you. Come with me, Dave. Hurry.'

She turned and ran along a dark passage. Ken staggered after her. His nose was bleeding and the lift had made a gash on his head. They went up some steps. Up more steps. 'Where is she taking me?' thought Ken. 'Is she going to turn me in?' But he was too dazed to think about it. It was all he could do to keep up with Pam.

At last a door swung open and Ken felt fresh air on his face. He was out in the moonlight. Loss of blood had made him dizzy but Pam was still beside him. Holding him up. Helping him along. 'It's not far to your flat,' she said. 'Do you think you can make it?' Ken thought, 'I should try to get away. Make a run for it.' But he was in no state to dash off. He couldn't walk — let alone run. He nodded. 'Yes,' he said. 'My flat.'

10

With Pam's help Ken got to his flat and staggered inside. There was no need to put the light on. The moon was shining in at the window. Ken made it to a chair. Then he passed out. It was three o'clock in the morning when Ken came round. Pam was still with him. She was washing the cut on his head. Her hands were soft on his skin. He opened his eyes and saw her pale, sweet face. It seemed to light the room.

As he looked at her one thought became clear in his mind. He was in love with Pam. He had loved her for days. For weeks. He had tried to push it out of his mind. To fool himself. But it was real. It had happened. He loved her. The thought was like a stabbing pain inside him. What could he do? What good was this love? He was a spy and Pam knew it. She was standing between him and freedom. If he could get away now he could still finish the job. Only one person was stopping him. Pam. The girl he loved.

Ken felt for his little black case. It should be at his side. Clipped to his belt. But where was it? Ken looked down and saw the broken clip. The case had gone. A cold dull feeling came over him. 'Oh God,' he said softly. 'My case . . . The film . . .' Pam knew what he was thinking and shook her head. 'I didn't take it,' she said. 'But I know where it is. It's lying at the bottom of the lift shaft. Forget it, Dave. If you try to go back for it I'll shoot you. I don't want to do it but I will if I have to.' There were tears in her eyes as she spoke. But she meant what she said. There was a gun in her hand.

'OK,' said Ken. 'You win. Now what are you going to do with me? Why not lock me up and get it over with?' He spoke coldly trying to hide his feelings. Trying to hide his love. Pam came closer to him. 'I won't do that,' she said. 'I don't need to. Don't you see? Your case is gone and that makes it easy for me. I couldn't let you walk out of here with that film. That would make *me* a spy as well. But now it's gone. It doesn't matter if you get away. I can help you.'

'I can't let you do that,' said Ken. 'It's too risky for you.' He took her hand but she pulled it away. 'Do you want to die?' she said. 'Look. I'll tell you what will happen. At 6.30 a.m. your case will be found. That's when the day staff check the lift. A hooter will boom out. Red lights will flash. The spy hunt will begin. Then they will find you and shoot you. I know, Dave. I've seen it all before. But if I help you, you can get away in time. You can take my car and when the main gate opens at 6.0 a.m. you can drive out of here.'

41

Ken ran his hand over his face. Had Pam gone mad? Or was she trying to trick him? The gunmen at the gate would never let him out. Then Ken saw the slip of paper in Pam's hand. It was a pass. A pass card stamped and dated. Ken's ticket to freedom. 'Thank 'Thank you, Pam,' he said softly. 'I can never repay you.'

With a flash of anger Pam said, 'I don't want you to repay me. I know you were just using me. Just playing a part. But my feelings were real. I was a fool.' Ken longed to say, 'I love you,' but he stopped himself. Pam thought he was just a con man. Let it stay that way. Her feelings for him must be dead by now. Already she must hate him. He looked down at himself. Looked at his PENTAG body. 'She's right,' he thought. 'I *am* a con man. The biggest con man of them all.' Feeling cold and ill he sat down on the floor. The cut on his head was beating like a drum. Suddenly he felt Pam's arms round him. 'I still love you,' she said softly. 'I don't know why. But I do. I can't help it.'

'You don't know me, Pam,' he said. 'My name isn't Dave West. I'm PENTAG spy H12. You don't know me at all.' Pam gave a little smile. 'Your name doesn't matter. It's *you* I care about.' Ken shook his head. He would tell her the truth. Yes. All of it. He owed it to her. 'It's not just my name,' he said. 'It's all of me.

Look at my face. Do you like it? Do you like my smile? Here, hold my hand. How does it feel?'

Pam didn't know what to say. She was shocked by the wild look in Ken's eyes. He held his hand in the air. 'It looks good. It feels good,' he said, *but it isn't mine.* It belongs to PENTAG. They gave me this body. Hands. Eyes. Teeth. Hair. It all belongs to PENTAG.'

Pam couldn't take it in. She sat staring at him with an odd blank look on her face. When the clock struck 4 it made Ken jump but Pam didn't move. 'The gate opens at 6,' thought Ken. 'I've got two hours left. I must talk to Pam. Make her understand.' He began to talk. Telling her all he could. Saying things he had never said to anyone before. Soon her eyes got brighter. Ken told her about Doctor ZB4. He told her what it was like to have a re-fit. A lot of his life was dim in his mind but he told her all he could.

Slowly the moon faded and daylight crept into the sky. At last Pam said, 'I understand. Thank you for telling me. Now can I see that photo? The old photo of you. I'd like to see it.' Ken got it and handed it to her. 'Here,' he said. 'It's in a bit of a mess. I've had it a long time.'

They both looked at the old, bent photo. At the young man with black hair and blue eyes. He smiled up at them from the paper. Smiled across the gap of years. Across time. Suddenly Ken shivered. The room seemed very chilly. 'I don't know why I keep that old thing,' he said. 'It's a photo of Ken Wilson. Not me. I *was* Ken Wilson a long time ago but not now.'

'Who are you now?' said Pam. 'That's the bit I don't understand. You aren't Dave West. You aren't Ken Wilson. Who are you?' She stood up and went over to the mirror. 'Look,' she said. 'That's *me* in the glass. My face and my body. I've got a flat with *my* things in it. I know all about *my* past. The things *I* did long ago. All this belongs to me. It's mine. Do you see? These things are part of me. They make me what I am.'

Pam turned to face Ken and her bright eyes seemed to cut into him. 'How about you?' she said. 'You haven't got any of these things. Don't you ever feel lost? Don't you ever say to yourself "who am I?"' Ken tapped his head. 'I'm here,' he said. 'Inside this skull. That's the real me. I don't need a lot of props around to tell me who I am. My body belongs to PENTAG but my *mind* belongs to me. Don't look so sad, Pam. I like it this way. I don't want to be stuck with one body and one life.'

Outside the window a bird began to sing. It was time to go. Time to say goodbye to Pam. A deep sadness filled Ken. He would miss her. 'Maybe,' he thought. 'Maybe I can come back one day. Just to see her.' But he knew it was foolish. This goodbye was for ever. He would never see her again.

He kissed Pam. Then he picked up the pass and the car keys. 'Don't forget your photo,' said Pam. Her eyes were bright with tears. 'You keep it,' said Ken. 'It's the only thing I've got that belongs to me. I'd like you to have it.' Quickly he turned and went out of the flat. Pam was left holding the old, torn photo.

Feeling dull and empty Ken set off down the steps. He had to pull himself together. Keep his wits about him. He wasn't safe yet. At the bottom of the steps he stopped. He thought he heard footsteps behind him. Was it Pam coming after him? With a smile on his lips he turned. Hoping to see her. But no one was there. He was alone.

Pam's car was parked just across the road. Ken took a few steps towards it, then he looked back. Was there someone . . .? No. He dashed across the road to the car. He didn't look back again. The footsteps ringing in his ears must be his own.

11

'So you just waved the pass and drove out of the gate?' said Doctor ZB4. Ken nodded. 'Yes, I met the pick-up team just as we planned and here I am. Back at Unit 5.' 'You were lucky,' said ZB4. 'That girl made it easy for you to get away. You can thank your good looking body for that.' He patted Ken's arm. 'Well, don't look so sad, H12. You lost the film but never mind. There will be other jobs. You can't will them all.'

The door behind Ken opened suddenly. It was only a girl with a tray of food but Ken jumped to his feet and spun round. 'Take it easy,' said the doctor. 'You are safe now.' Ken sat down and ran his hand over his face. ZB4 could see that he was upset. 'What's the matter?' he said. 'Is something bothering you?'

'No . . . Yes,' said Ken. 'Oh I don't know. I've just got an odd feeling. I've had it for a long time. I keep thinking that someone is following me. As I drove away in the car I kept looking back. But I didn't see anyone.' 'Maybe it was that girl,' said the doctor. 'Maybe she planned to let you go and then follow you.' Ken shook his head. 'No. Anyway I had this feeling before I met her. Before I did the last job. Am I being a fool? Or is there someone after me?'

The doctor sucked his cheeks in and thought for a bit. 'You could be right,' he said. 'It isn't easy to track down a PENTAG spy, but now and then it happens. Maybe someone *has* been following you. But don't let it upset you. I'll give you a re-fit tomorrow. That's what you need. A new face. A new body. You'll be safe inside it. When I've fixed you up, you can have a rest. I'll send you to a little hide-out in the hills. A nice spot. How about that?' 'It sounds fine,' said Ken. 'Thanks, doctor.'

Slowly Ken made his way to the rest room and flopped down on a bed. He shut his eyes and tried to sleep. But it was no good. Thoughts were going round and round inside his head. He had to face a re-fit tomorrow. Yes, tomorrow. So soon. Sadly he got up and went to the big mirror at the end of the room. He wanted to take a last look at himself. This was the man that Pam Liston had fallen in love with. The fine tall body. The dazzling smile. Tomorrow it would all be gone. Tomorrow the doctor's cunning hands would pull Dave West apart and shape a new body.

Ken rested his cheek on the cold glass of the mirror. This body was his last link with Pam. After today she wouldn't know him. Not even if she met him face to face. 'I love her,' thought Ken. 'I'll always love her. I won't have the same name or the same body. But the real me will go on loving her. The real me will never forget her.'

The next day Ken had his re-fit. When it was over he lay in a deep sleep. More than a week slipped by, then at last Ken began to wake up. Slowly he pulled himself out of the net of sleep. Very slowly he opened his eyes. He felt like a swimmer coming up from the bottom of the sea. Doctor ZB4 was standing by the bed. Ken turned to look at him. 'Is that you, ZB4?' he said. 'I can't see you very well. You are just a blur.'

'You need your glasses,' said ZB4. 'Here. I'll put them on for you.' With the glasses Ken could see better. He pushed back the blankets and looked down at himself. A thin body. Thin and bent. ZB4 helped him out of bed and handed him a walking stick. Ken took it and went slowly across to the mirror. He peered at the face in the glass. Looked at the sagging skin. The flabby lips. The pink gums. No teeth. No hair. He was an old man.

'It's not much to look at,' said ZB4. 'But it will do for now. If someone has been following you this body will throw him off the track.' Ken nodded. Then he rubbed his glasses. He could see a thick red scar on his neck and a spot of raw skin on his leg. Don't worry about that,' said the doctor. 'I did this body in a bit of a rush and it's not very neat. Still, it will heal up. Have a good rest at the hide-out, H12. When you come back you will be fit for the next job. By the way your new name is Ben Smith."

Ken wasn't really awake yet. In a daze he sat down on the bed and began to mutter his new name. Ben Smith. Ben Smith. Soon a girl came in and got him ready for the trip. She washed him. Dressed him. Ken let her do it. All this seemed like part of a dream. He was still lost in a fog of sleep when the pick-up team came to take him to the plane.

12

The sun was sinking behind the hills. Rays of soft red light fell on the trees and the grass. Shadows were creeping across the lake and across the little log hut on the hillside. This was a PENTAG hide-out and Ken was sitting inside the hut looking at the sunset.

A deep sadness hung over him. 'Why do I feel like this?' he thought. 'I must unpack my things. Make myself at home. That will cheer me up.' With old stiff fingers he undid his case. One by one he took the things out and put them on the bed. The pile grew and soon the case was empty. 'Is this stuff mine?' thought Ken. 'This pipe?' These slippers? Do they belong to me?' He limped over to the big dusty mirror on the wall and wiped it. There in the glass was the sagging face of Ben Smith. 'Yes, they are mine,' he thought. Sadly he put the things away.

Soon the sun slipped behind the hills and the shadows got longer and darker. 'I'm all alone,' thought Ken. 'There is no one near. No one for miles. Just me.' Suddenly he was afraid. He felt mixed up and lonely. Something was missing from his life. What was it? He tried to think back.

Bits of the past came to him. Little scraps. Like rags
blowing in the wind. He could see a girl's face. Young
Pretty. Who was she? He dug about in the past trying
to think of her name. Was it Pat? Or Ann? It was no
good. His last re-fit had wiped it out. Slowly Ken went
back to the mirror and looked at himself again. 'No,'
he thought. 'She's nothing to do with me. I don't
know her.'

It was dark now and the wind was getting up. It made
a low hollow sound as it blew round the hut. Dead
leaves hit the window. Tapping like hand on the glass.
Ken locked the door and stood shivering. He was
afraid. He didn't feel safe any more. Best to go to bed.
Get some sleep. Forget about the dark night and the
howling wind. It would all be better in the morning.

Quickly Ken undressed. His old head sank deep in
the soft pillow and the blankets made a snug nest
round his body. Soon he was asleep. But he got no
rest. Out of the waves of sleep came a dream. Faces
rose up under his closed eyelids. All the faces that
had belonged to him. Bob Harris. Mike Skipton. Dave
West. Ben Smith. Other faces that had been his long
ago.

They all pressed round him smiling. In his dream
Ken backed away. 'What do you want?' he called.

One by one the faces came near and spoke to him. One by one they said, 'You know me. But who are you? Who are you?' Ken tried to run but the dream faces blocked his way. They crowded together. They melted. They mixed. They became one face. One big face. And it was blank. No eyes. No nose. Just smooth skin.

Ken yelled out loud and woke up with a jerk. Rain was beating on the windows of the hut. The wind was howling like a dog in pain. 'It was just a dream,' thought Ken. 'I'm awake now. It's over.' But it wasn't over. As Ken looked at the door the bolt moved. Was it the wind? Or was there someone outside? Was someone slowly working the bolt back in its socket?

Ken fell from the bed and staggered to the window. He could see a shape. A dark shape. A man was standing outside the hut. Near the door. Waiting. 'I knew it,' thought Ken. 'I was right all the time. Someone *was* after me. Someone followed me from body to body. Tracked me down. Now he's here and I'm trapped.' Ken looked down at his old weak body. It was no good trying to run away. He must face the man.

With shaking hands Ken put the light on. Then he got his gun. 'Now,' he thought, 'this is the end for one of us. It's him or me.' He limped to the door and pulled back the bolt. A blast of wind hit him and he fired into the storm. Fired at the shadowy shape. It didn't move. Ken fired again. A flash of light lit the sky and Ken saw the tall outline of the man.

'Come here,' Ken yelled. 'Come and get me. I know you have been following me. Well. here I am.' Slowly the man came nearer. He had no gun. His hands were by his sides. The light from the hut fell on his feet. On his legs. On his body. 'I know him,' thought Ken. 'Who is he?' The rays of light fell on the man's face. His blue eyes shone. His black hair gleamed in the light. Ken stared. Stared in panic. It was his own face. The face he was born with. The face of Ken Wilson.

Ken reeled back into the hut and a thin cry came from his lips. 'It's me,' he thought. 'It's me. But it can't be. I'm . . . I'm . . . Who am I?' Panic gripped him. He didn't know any more. He didn't know who he was. 'Help me, someone,' he called. 'Tell me who I am.'

Something was happening to him. Something inside him was snapping. Falling apart. Melting. What could he do? Wildly he looked round the room. He saw the mirror. Yes. Yes. The mirror. Across the spinning room he went. Across to the glass. Now what could he see? What was it? Horror filled his cracking mind. There was *no one* in the mirror. No face. No body. No one at all. Just the room. The empty room. Where was he? Where had he gone?

Thunder crashed over the empty hut and the howling wind spoke to the trees. 'No one . . . nowhere . . . nothing,' it said.

Blood on t__

by David Cook

Other works by the author:

The Soldier Chronicles series
Liberty or Death
Heart of Oak

Blood on the Snow
David Cook
Copyright © David Cook 2014

It was dawn in Holland.

Under a blue-grey winter sky, a column of soldiers marched across frozen crop fields. Snow had fallen during the night, and in the morning, the world had become a crunchy white bleakness. The wind whistled as it whipped across the fields, ice hung from fence posts and sheeted the tufts of grass so that each blade looked as though it was encased in glass. The bare furrows were hard and slippery, puddles were iced-over, and the men's breath plumed above their heads.

The soldiers were from a company of the 28th, a British regiment raised in North Gloucestershire, and their destination was a farmstead half a mile away. The feeble sun clung to the horizon, throwing their rushing shadows far ahead of them like a newspaper's exaggerated caricatures. The wind tugged snow from the ground, whirling it in a glittering dance, and straight into their faces.

Most of them wore their thick issue greatcoats, but some were without winter dress altogether. The British army had suffered horrendously from the Flanders climate; the men's coats had literally fallen apart. Some redcoats had been issued with simple jackets without any lace and facings as replacements, some wore local homespun jackets that looked crude and ill-fashioned, and some even wore clogs made from willow-wood, because their boots had rotted away. The unlucky ones, without the winter coats and gloves, had tied scraps of cloth around their hands and bare feet. The smart bright red of the uniform had long faded to a dull purple, or pink, and was now so heavily patched with mismatched cloth that the men resembled vagabonds rather than soldiers. Their unshaven faces were wrapped in scarves made from common sacking, or what they had looted and begged along the way. Some had lost their black round hats, and either wore forage, or simple peasant hats tied in place under the chin with twine.

Their vacant expressions and sunken cheeks, made dirty through weeks of campaigning, betrayed that they were exhausted and bitterly hungry.

The Duke of York's British and German Army had joined their Austrian and Dutch allies by landing in the Austrian-owned Netherlands, and had marched expecting an easy victory. But the French, swept away with their new republicanism, had turned on them with an unforgiving fury, speed and superior numbers. Defeat after defeat had left the British fighting alone, but the winter brought more misery, and they were forced to retreat across the frozen Gelderland in the fervent hope of reaching the harbours in the north where ships would take them home.

They had marched for days. It was a struggle with the roads being flooded, iced over, or left as glutinous traps. Time after time, they had stopped and waited while a gun carriage, or wagon was shifted by brute force. Rain and snow fell with barely a break, and the few Dutch they saw stared at them with suspicious eyes. There were no cheers of welcome for their allies. There was nothing but marching, pain and cold.

An officer, mounted on a black charger, trotted to the front of the company; the horse whinnied, hot steam pluming from its wide nostrils. He looked ashen and seemed to wince in rhythm to the horse's stride.

'Damn your haste!' he said angrily. 'What's the hurry, man? Do you need to void your bowels?' His comments were directed to an officer who marched confidently ahead of the men.

'We're late, sir,' the officer said reproachfully. He was a lieutenant and just stared ahead rather than turn to his superior.

Flecks of snow dotted his bicorn hat and his long chestnut-coloured hair that was tied back with a frayed black bow.

Captain Andrew Clements hawked once and then spat onto the ground. 'Late? Late for what exactly? You have a whore waiting for you, Lieutenant? Is that it?' He had an insolent face, cold and antagonistic. He held a canteen to his mouth, gulped and then wiped his unshaven chin that bristled with white hairs.

Lieutenant Jack Hallam ignored the remark. He knew that the canteen contained rum and that Clements was already drunk.

He usually was.

'Pick your feet up, Private Tipton,' Sergeant Abraham Fox bellowed. 'I've seen Dutch girls who are more soldierly than you are!' Fox was a dark-eyed, burly man, and his face was a horror of ancient scars. He turned to the rest of the company. 'Pick up your stride, all of you!'

'That's the way, Sergeant,' Clements said, hiccupped and then burped. 'Onward, you laggard scum!'

Hallam glanced behind; the men marched quietly and solemnly. They might look like beaten tramps, but the 28th had spent the last two weeks fighting a rear-guard that had astounded even the most cynical adversaries and brought praise from the generals. Men may have died in their dozens from the miasmic fever caused by the swampy countryside, and crippled by frostbite, but the despondency in the men of Number Eight Company was irrevocably due to Clements.

The forty-year-old captain frowned constantly as if everything bothered him. He had dark hair turning white, protuberant eyes, and such a languid demeanour that he always appeared to slouch. His family was exceedingly wealthy and owned a thousand acres of woodland in the Forest of Dean, but he was never one for sharing such personal information, especially to his fellow officers. A month ago the brusque captain had ordered Private Wheeler to be flogged for suspected thievery of a pocket watch. However, it turned out that the popular private had not been the culprit and died from his wounds, caused by the four hundred given lashes. It became apparent that Clements had simply misplaced his watch, after all, and Wheeler had died for nothing. The captain was never reprimanded and that galled Hallam severely. Clements verbally abused the men, even more so when he was drunk, so the remarks were frequent and daily. And so by now, December 1794, morale, already strained, had dipped to an all-time low.

Hallam knew the men deserved better than contempt, and when Clements was indisposed, he personally took command and encouraged and praised them. The captain had once told him querulously that the ranks were filled with 'every deplorable piece of refuse imaginable'. To control and forge the men into the professional soldier's hours of monotonous drill and harsh punishments were relied upon. There had been a skirmish a few days back and the men had performed admirably; every movement had been a drill-master's delight and every command was obeyed crisply as though they were performing on parade for the Duke of York. Clements paid them no heed. He had sat scowling from his saddle, no doubt suffering from a hangover, but Hallam had congratulated them and witnessed a spark of appreciation. It wasn't much; a tiny flicker of gratitude, but it was a start and one he wanted to build on.

Footsteps hurried towards Hallam. 'Did the captain call your wife a whore, sir?' Ensign Julian Stubbington asked tentatively, as the captain had slowed his horse to a mere walk in order to top up his canteen with a small bottle. One of the horse's hind legs was wrapped in a cloth, and the beast juddered due to an infection.

'No, he did not,' Hallam replied irritably, although his exasperation was directed at Clements, now further down the line.

Hallam was from Wendover in Buckinghamshire and at twenty-nine was newly married. He had met Isabel at a ball held in her home town of Lyndhurst, in the New Forest, when the battalion was on standby to join the army in March of this year. He hated such occasions. He disliked dancing, had no interest in small talk, but as soon as they were introduced he had felt his heart strings being pulled. Soon, they had both fallen deeply in love.

Isabel was a thin girl, not yet twenty, beautiful, loving, and considerate. He absolutely adored her – physically and spiritually. They got married in a tiny parish church on a beautiful day, just six weeks after meeting, and just days before the regiment had sailed away. He remembered the parting; she had kissed him hard, her tongue shimmering, exhilarating and loving as she curled it around his. She drew back, eyes glinting with tears.

'Come back to me, Jack,' Isabel had pleaded. 'Please come back.'

He had held her tightly, not wanting to let her go. 'I will, my love. I promise.'

Hallam brought out a silver locket from his pocket. It gleamed brightly despite the morning's bleak sunlight. He had it made for the wedding. Inside was a small miniature of her portrait. He touched her softly painted face with a finger nail. It still felt odd being married, even after eight months, but it was a good feeling nonetheless.

The company numbered thirty-five and were alone in the silent wintry landscape. The other nine companies that made up the regiment were somewhere to the north, and somewhere behind was the vanguard of the French. It was a world of pitiless torture, empty bellies, and the daily slog of discipline-destroying withdrawal.

'Are we lost, sir?' Stubbington asked. His face was red and his lips were severely chapped from the biting wind. He had turned sixteen on the voyage over and came from Deerhurst, a small village on the eastern bank of the River Severn.

'No.'

'It's just that I can't make head or tail of where we're heading to, sir,' he said, glancing at the brown ruined stalks of old crops. 'Every field, every village and every wood looks the same as the last one.'

Hallam pointed at the farm with a black-nailed finger. Early morning mist cloaked a stream in pale skeins that ran parallel to it. The sky was still dark to the west.

'See that, Mister Stubbington?' he asked. 'That's where we're supposed to be.'

The ensign strained to see the dwelling, because it was snowing again. He could make out the tall beech, alder and oak trees that surrounded the farm, but very little else. There was a dark glassy patch of ground and Stubbington considered that it was a lake of sorts.

'That's where we were supposed to be last night.' Hallam could not keep the bitterness from his voice.

7

Lieutenant-Colonel Edward Paget had ordered Number Seven, Eight and the Grenadier Companies to attack a French held bridge. Paget was just eighteen and wanted to make a name for himself and his new regiment. He personally sent the three companies forward in the dark, urging the men on in his usual high spirits. However, his hope of an easy victory turned, like the rest of the campaign, into a debacle. Clements had kept the company back when the assault started, then bungled the advance so that the company missed out on the initial attack. Luckily, the redcoats were eventually able to eject the minor French force from the bridge after sustaining a well-timed musket volley. The enemy then retreated east to their battle lines.

The young colonel wasn't best pleased. He congratulated the other two companies on their success, but Clements was ordered south to the farm to wait for further orders. Hallam knew that they had been dismissed as Paget had no valid reason to send them out from the parent battalion. He just wanted to rid of them as though their failure was infectious.

Number Eight Company was deemed a hopeless cause under the mismanagement of Clements. His ineptitude had left the company lost in the dark as they struggled to find the farmstead in the endless patchwork of fields. As night fell, Hallam had found a barn, and despite Clements' constant grumbling, the men had been able to at least find shelter and warmth.

Hallam was in a foul mood. He was looking to snap at everything, in Stubbington's opinion, and the young ensign was rarely wrong about his lieutenant. He knew well enough from previous conversations that the best notion was not to engage in one, but Stubbington was infectiously cheerful and difficult to be swayed by bad moods.

'Is it true that the farm is called Buggenum, sir?'

'Yes,' Hallam said wearily, as he knew what the ensign was going to say next.

'Funny name for a farm,' the ensign said after a while. 'Sounds a bit like 'bugger', doesn't it?'

Hallam ignored him.

'It's not the captain's fault, sir,' Stubbington changed the subject. He wiped a grey coat sleeve under his runny nose.

'What?'

'It's not his fault that we got lost.'

Hallam turned and narrowed his flint-grey eyes on the young officer. 'Who's bloody fault do you suppose it is then?'

Stubbington shrank back from Hallam's gaze rather than his reply. He stumbled on the slick and treacherous road, but managed to stop himself from tumbling over. 'What I mean to say, sir, is that he drinks to forget a hardship.'

'What the hell does that mean?'

The ensign adjusted his felt hat. He had tied a strip of blue cloth around his head to stop the round hat from spilling over his eyes; the cloth was always visible underneath. 'My father, God bless him for his sins, is a physician, and he once told me that some men drink to overcome personal loss. Women and finances and such like,' he said, shrugging as though that explained the way of the world. 'He'd seen it many times. They always take to drink, he would say. I suppose the drink is a comfort in dark times. Personally, I can't understand why, when a mug of steaming tea does the trick.'

'The captain is neither hurting nor taking comfort, Mister Stubbington,' Hallam said quietly and dismissively, because Clements had spurred his horse near them. 'He's idle and bored. That's why he drinks.'

'Perhaps the colonel could impose a drinking ban?' the young officer suggested. 'It might help the rank and file too, who I notice spend every waking moment on the stuff?'

Hallam glared at him. 'Stop the men from drinking? Soldiers will drink as fish will swim. It's preposterous to suggest such a thing.' He thought about asking why the ensign had not followed in his father's footsteps, but bit off any inclination.

Stubbington looked glumly at the farm where the lake was more visible. He wondered whether there might be any fowl in amongst the reeds, with the intriguing thought of catching the birds for tonight's dinner. The water was frozen and was the colour of ploughshares. 'I'm sorry, sir,' he tried to assuage his captain.

Hallam cast the ensign a fleeting look, realising he had replied too callously. 'Most of them only joined up for drink, Mister Stubbington. You'd have a mutiny on your hands if you took it

9

away. It's a shameful thing to say, but it's true. Half the officers I know will be drunk as I speak. Good ones too.'

Stubbington suspected that Hallam was not referring to Clements. 'Yes, sir.'

'But things are going to change.'

'Oh? Why?'

'Because there's going to be a battle,' Hallam said, rubbing his hands with relish. The snow was falling thicker, and there was a silence only punctuated by the sound of the men breathing and boots crunching.

The ensign went as white as cartridge paper. 'B-battle?' he stammered.

'Yes, Mister Stubbington,' Hallam said grinning. 'A good old-fashioned fight that will sort the wheat from the chaff. I can feel it in my very marrow. It's what this company needs. It's what the battalion needs. Jesus, it's what the whole goddamned army needs. If we're not fighting then we're not winning. Our lads need a morale boost. A proper fight will give them that.'

Hallam welcomed a good fight. It's what the men were paid to do and it's what they wanted to do. After months of doing nothing in Flanders but retreat, dither and then retreat again, the army had moved from one calamity to the next. The commanders were too busy fighting over their laurels and trying to pull rank over one another. Senior battalion officers blamed everyone except themselves for their own mistakes, the sergeants seemed to run the companies because most of the officers were drunk, jaded and lax in their duties. The rank and file were simply depressed.

Ever since the Battle of Fleurus in June, where the French had defeated a tired and ill-managed Austrian and Dutch army under Prince Saxe-Coburg, the French Revolutionary soldiers had beaten and outflanked the allies in almost every skirmish. They fought like devils and it left the British Army a forlorn, dejected and dispirited mass of men.

'The Slashers will show the French upstarts how Englishmen fight!' Hallam said, using the regiment's nickname. The 28th had been on garrison duty in Canada and a malicious lawyer regularly upset some of the men and their families, so some of them broke into

10

his home and slashed the man's ear off in retaliation. The lawyer never said another hostile word and the guilty men were never found. The regiment showed the world that everyone cared for each other, just like a family, and to this day they were proud of that ferocious nickname.

'Yes, sir.' Stubbington tried to sound confident, but somehow managed to only increase the pitch of his voice. Hallam glared at him briefly before turning away.

There was going to be a battle, and the company, Hallam reflected brightly, might well be his by tomorrow's sundown.

****

A black dog barked incessantly at the approaching redcoats from the farm gates until it was silenced with a brutal kick. It ran back to the house, whimpering. There was a clatter of hooves and Major Osborne, mounted on his fine bay horse, appeared at the gates.

'Ah, good to see you, Clements,' he shouted the jocular greeting in his usual hoarse voice, but his expression was hardly welcoming. He was pinch-faced, with heavy bags under red-rimmed eyes. 'We thought we'd lost you. Well, at least the colonel hoped so,' he added with a sneering guffaw.

'Not lost, sir,' Clements said. 'I just took the company on manoeuvres.'

'What?' Osborne was incredulous. His horse bared its teeth and pawed the air as though it was uneasy, and he instinctively patted its neck with a gloved hand. Clements, the major and the colonel were the only officers Hallam knew who had not lost their horses to the campaign.

'Yes, sir,' Clements continued the lie, then turned briefly in his saddle to order the company to halt, before turning sharply back to the major. 'It's always good to get the men up early for manoeuvres. It keeps them keen and alert.'

Osborne gave a bewildered shake of his head. 'What an appalling notion.' He curbed an urge to drink the fine claret, which he had just taken from the house and that made him feel irritable. He drummed his fingers on the stiff leather saddle's pommel instead.

11

In the courtyard a group of redcoats were handling several bags, and one or two paintings. A private with an angry red boil on his cheek, held something in his hands and Hallam saw a flash of silver before it disappeared into a sack. Two men were carrying a heavy oak chest with some difficulty. Pockets and haversacks were crammed with goods, bellies were plugged with whatever food was found and heads were foggy with plundered alcohol.

'What's going on here, sir?' Hallam asked suspiciously.

'Naught that concerns you,' Osborne said nastily.

Captain Pulmer from Number Four Company walked out from one of the buildings. He looked surprised to see Clements. A bolt of red silk was under an arm.

'Nothing left for you, Andrew,' he said cheerfully, but then was silenced by a grunt from the major.

'What about the owners, sir?' Hallam asked Osborne. 'Are they home?'

Osborne, his mouth tight, looked at him with a deliberate slowness. 'So what if they are?'

So he had been plundering the farm with Pulmer's men. Hallam thought it disgraceful. Clements, he noted, showed no objection, but was probably jealous that he missed out.

'It's not right.'

The major looked infuriated. 'What did you say?'

'I said it's not right,' Hallam repeated obstinately.

'I don't give a damn what you think, Lieutenant.' Osborne glowered at him. Pulmer sneered at the rebuke. 'They are French sympathisers and conspirators. A troop of dragoons were seen leaving here yesterday. All the damned Dutch are in league with the Jacobins, so I'll not have another word said about the matter.' He turned to the swaggering Pulmer. 'Let us leave this place. Our young new colonel is expecting us and he cannot abide lateness,' he said scathingly. 'Besides, there's a wood nearby where deer have been spotted in abundance. I fancy a spot of hunting. Bring back some venison for my Christmas dinner, eh?' He trotted away, before glaring at Hallam.

Pulmer walked away looking smug. The man was a notorious braggart and troublemaker, and Hallam scowled at his retreating back. He turned to step through the gates into the courtyard as the last of Pulmer's men filed past. A corporal had a hen with its neck wrung tied to his pack and another was cutting the canvas away from a gilt picture frame with his bayonet. A Gobelin tapestry of the Virgin Mary was ripped in two to make ridiculous cloaks. Four privates were bickering over a bottle of brandy, their language coarse and threats brazen. It slipped from their grasp to smash onto the road. One of the privates bent down to guzzle up the liquid, lapping at it like a dog. A puddle of horse urine steamed on icy cobbles. Several books lay scattered, the pages flapping in the wind.

Hallam walked to the far end of the courtyard, which led to what was once the stable block. It had been months since it had last been in proper use and only the faintest of odours lingered. The smell of horses, leather and dung was fresher upon standing in the stalls. Just a few days before it had served as a billet to another British regiment. They had chopped up the last remaining doors and shutters to burn.

The house itself was long and low and was painted red with green shutters and frames. A large barn faced southwards, the roof thatch now lost to folds of crisp snow. Hallam could make out a piggery and a large henhouse. Beyond the barn and nestled in amongst bare trees was a smaller barn, a dairy and a windmill. It was certainly a prosperous and busy farm; a wide track wound around the distant trees and onto the meadows where the dairy herd would be taken to pasture across the stream. Hallam turned back to the house. The front door was open, splintered, which revealed it had been forced. One of the windows was smashed. He could hear muffled cries coming from somewhere inside.

'Where do you think you're going?' Clements enquired as Hallam walked towards the door. 'Lieutenant! Come back here!'

Hallam ignored him and, upon entering the house, found himself in a long, white-painted hallway. To the right was the kitchen and pantry; to the left a parlour with a large stone chimney and windows that in the summer overlooked a large rectangular flowerbed where roses, rhododendrons and persicaria might bloom in magnificent colour.

'Hello?' his voice echoed.

13

He waited. There was no answer, but he could still hear crying upstairs.

'Hello?' he said again, louder.

The place looked as though it had been stripped of anything of value. Drawers from a small writing desk lay broken on the floor and papers were scattered everywhere. The scullery and kitchen had been raided of all foodstuffs. Pots and bowls were strewn everywhere.

Hallam heard footsteps. He looked up to see a young woman, who was obviously the maid, coming down the stairs. She was blonde with a high forehead and blood from a wound had crusted dark on her scalp. She was adjusting her clothes. He didn't know what to say.

'Miss, do you need help?'

The woman jumped because she had not seen him. '*Wat doet U hier nog? Vertrek!*' she shouted angrily at him.

'I'm sorry, Miss, I don't understand,' he said removing his weather-beaten hat. 'Do you speak English?' He heard another woman moan. He glanced upstairs, but could see no one. 'Does your mistress require assistance?'

The maid spat at him. '*Ga weg!*'

'Please tell your mistress that I am sorry.' Hallam stared at the blood that matted her hair. 'Can I help you? Is there anyone else hurt?' He wondered where the males of the household were.

The girl gestured for him to leave. '*Vertrek!*' she shouted at him again, then began to cry.

Hallam hesitantly moved to the doorway after deciding he was not wanted. Then he was struck with a thought. He removed his purse from inside his coat and jacket. 'Please,' he said kindly, 'tell your mistress that I leave this payment with my sincerest apologies for the damage and theft.' He placed the money, which amounted to little over three pounds, on the sideboard next to an ornament. It wouldn't cover the loss but it was the bulk of his available funds. He bowed once before leaving amidst another yell of hostility.

'You have a way with the women, Lieutenant,' Clements said, laughing at his ire. He burped and clicked his horse forward.

Stubbington ran over to Hallam. 'What's going on, sir? Is there a lady in there?'

'We're leaving; that's what's going on,' Hallam said furiously as he strode across the courtyard taking in the smell of animal dung, leather tack and unwashed flesh. 'How in God's name will the men learn what's right from wrong when the officers are corrupt! Goddamn Pulmer!'

'Sir?' Stubbington had difficulty in keeping up with Hallam's long stride.

'Sergeant Fox!' Hallam called abruptly.

'Sir!'

Hallam went to speak disrespectfully of Clements in front of the men, then quickly bit it off. 'Where's the captain?'

Stubbington gazed down the road. 'He's with the major, sir.'

Hallam swore fluently and impressively and didn't care who heard him. 'Get the men ready, Sergeant,' he said fiercely. 'We're leaving for Rotheheim, and any bastard that isn't on his feet in one minute will be left behind! The French love handling pricks so they'll be overjoyed to acquire a few more.'

The two sergeants and two corporals immediately rousted the men. Fox kicked Tipton. 'Don't lounge there like an expectant whore, boy! Get up like the captain ordered!'

Corporal Beckett slapped a man across the face to wake him, but the private was already in the drunken throes of unconsciousness.

'Leave the bastard,' Hallam said callously. 'And take note of his name and offence for the records.'

'Sir,' Beckett said, leaving the man on the roadside.

A private went to drag his unfortunate companion up, but Hallam stopped him. 'I said leave him!' Beckett pushed the other redcoat back into his file.

Stubbington bent down to the road to one side to pick up a blue feather that had been tossed aside during the plunder. The young officer had a penchant for anything coloured blue and seemed delighted to wear it in his hat.

'You're a regular dandy now, sir,' Private Daniel Tipton said as the company marched swiftly away. He sneezed and, pressing a

15

finger against on nostril, blew a string of green snot from the other. 'Best dressed one I've ever seen.'

Stubbington, immensely pleased at the comment, bowed at the private. 'Me thinks somewhere there is a young Dutch girl in need of rescue,' he said, standing in what he considered a heroic pose. 'Come hither, girl, to your Romeo.' He puffed up his thin chest like a winter robin. A ripple of bawdy laughter reached their lieutenant.

'Quiet in the ranks!' Hallam snapped. 'Get back to your place, Mister Stubbington.'

'Sir!' the boy obeyed, but his cheerfulness was not quashed by Hallam's temperament.

'March, you bastards!' Hallam set the company a brutal pace. He could hear their complaints, but ignored them. He knew from experience, having tried one on once, how the wooden frames of the backpacks pressed painfully against the spine, and the tight straps constricted the chest until each breath was raw. 'Marching and a rare fight will banish the chill from your bones. You'll thank me one day. Why? Because believe it not, I want you all to live.'

If the army had been shattered by the dreadful weather; where the wind cut flesh like a dragoon's sword and men froze to death in their sleep, then there were still some men who marched, even in defeat, in good formation and with good discipline. Private Matthew Hulse was one. Tall, reedy and with thinning hair, he was always respectful and eloquent. An intelligent man ruined by drink. Caught stealing liquor, he had enlisted to save himself from the gallows. He helped Fox run the company books.

Private James Shawford was another. A big man, in fact so big, he should have belonged in the Grenadier Company, and was a professional soldier. With a dozen or more years in the regiment, he was an old hand, and the recruits looked up to him. Impassive at times, and brutal in combat, Shawford had beaten to death a man with his own hands before escaping to the army at fifteen years old.

It was men like these, Hallam considered, that kept the regiment from dissolving into chaos.

They soon caught up with Pulmer's men, but Hallam marched his company off the road to go around them so that Clements was left with Osborne, who shrugged and cursed him.

16

Hallam could just about see a pall of thick dark smoke from two miles away. A farm was burning. Or was it a house in the town? He wiped flakes from his eyes; his eyebrows were frosted white. He peered again, but the sky was darkening and the snowfall was turning to a horrid cold sleet. He shivered, the raw wind sinking its teeth into his marrow. This was a land where snow thickened in the dikes and ditches and, when there was a thaw, it came as drizzling sheets that made the conditions even more unbearable.

They followed the road northwards. It was fairly straight and flanked by some of the tallest trees Hallam had ever seen. Mostly oaks and birch, and in the summer he considered, this avenue full of plump green boughs would be a place of beauty. He remembered the tulip fields in the west of the country. What a sight! There had been acres of them. A man had once told him that Lincolnshire was like Holland, flat with large open fens, tulips and windmills. Hallam had scoffed at the notion; declaring it too foreign.

Now the great trees stood like ghosts and the flowers long dead under a frozen blanket. The sun, a glint in the melancholy sky, spat bitter embers.

The men were quiet, no doubt dreaming of warmth, food and women. Hallam tried to remember the last time he had eaten a hot meal. A week ago? Or was it two?

The British Army had suffered appalling supply problems from the start of the campaign. Food was often delivered late and was inedible by the 'Newgate Blues', the mocking nickname given for the Royal Corps of Waggoners, who were considered to be criminals. They skimmed the best of the supplies and sold it at a profit to the markets at Amsterdam, Ostend and Antwerp. But now the commissariat had completely disintegrated because the French had savagely forced the British to retreat from the ports, and the soldiers were left ravenous.

'Sir?'

'What do you want, Mister Stubbington?' The wind instantly snatched Hallam's breath away.

Stubbington proffered Hallam a white-toothed smile. 'I wanted to ask about Captain Clements, sir.'

Hallam frowned. 'What about him?'

'Are we going to leave him?'

'Bugger him,' Hallam remarked scornfully. He pulled out a timepiece that Isabel's father had given to him as a wedding gift. 'In thirty minutes, we'll be at the town where the colonel will be waiting for us. He can't abide tardiness and I want to show him how to run a company,' he said.

On the outskirts of Rotheheim, the road dipped slightly and the company had to cross an ice-crusted stone bridge over a frozen stream to get to the town that was smeared with the haze of dark smoke. A smattering of skeleton-like trees edged the road where rooks croaked and mistletoe grew in clumps.

Redcoats watched their arrival. There were men from the 27th, the Inniskillings Irish rogues to a man who wore buff facings. A couple of them were drinking heavily, but they let Hallam and his men past without causing any trouble. A tall officer with sandy hair, a broken nose and sabre-scarred face nodded to him, and Hallam returned the greeting. It seemed that he was keeping a close eye on his men and he certainly looked as though he could handle even the most disobedient of them.

There were scores of civilians, horses and carts in the town's square. A blue-plume of smoke roiled from a burnt wreck of a building across the road that Hallam had seen. A couple of windows were smashed on some of the houses. Icicles hung from lintels. Redcoats from another regiment were forming up ahead of the crowd.

'Lieutenant Hallam!' a voice called him.

Hallam swivelled on his heels. It was Colonel Paget who was mounted on his fine horse.

'Sir,' he saluted.

'Where's Captain Clements?' Paget looked severe as he trotted over.

Hallam jerked his head back towards the bridge. 'He's with Major Osborne and Captain Pulmer's company, sir.'

Paget said nothing for a moment. 'What was Captain Pulmer doing back there?' he asked, wrinkling his nose from the snuff he'd just taken. He was addicted to it. He paused, then sneezed violently.

'Sir?' Hallam said impassively, feigning ignorance. Was his loyalty being tested? He wasn't loyal to Osborne and Pulmer, and certainly not Clements, but he would not openly spread gossip.

Paget watched him for a second, just as a hawk might watch its prey, before deciding whatever he intended to say would remain unheard. 'I won't have any men from the regiment looting from the Dutch when they are our allies,' he said, glaring at Pulmer's men who were just approaching the bridge.

Hallam didn't know what to say. How had the colonel known?

Paget fixed them a hard stare that spoke of disapproval. 'I won't have the regiments' good name dragged through the mud because a few officers can't keep their men in check. Roaming and pouncing like a pack of bloody wolves. It won't do, Jack.'

It's not the men that are the real problem; it's the officers, Hallam said to himself. He liked Paget because he was morally strong and incorruptible, and although he was so young, he had the maturity and shrewdness of a much older wiser man. He might be new and thought unkindly by Osborne as a mere wet-behind-the-ears boy, but he cared deeply for the regiment and was more of an officer and gentleman than the pugnacious major could ever be.

'What's happening here, sir?'

'We're burning one of our depots,' Paget replied as a gust of wind caught the smoke to cloud the street black. 'Can't take the stuff with us and we certainly can't let the Crapauds have it, so we have no options but to burn it. All of it.' The smoke was stinging his eyes. 'Are your men ready, Jack?' he asked, scanning his watery eyes over the company. Stubbington tried to look alert.

'Always, sir.'

'Good, because we're going north to bolster our defences and push the French back across the Waal.'

'They've crossed it?' Hallam was taken aback by the news.

Paget answered with a gentle nod of his head. 'Last night. It took our forward sentries by complete surprise. They didn't need the bridges after all. Crafty buggers just walked across the ice. Humbugged us, by God. So we're burning unwanted stores and leaving now.'

19

'Jesus.' Hallam was shocked. The British had thought that the River Waal, a natural defensive obstacle that swept across the land, would halt any French progress until Spring. The main bridges had been destroyed, or those left standing were heavily defended, but the French now threatened to cut off the British rear-guard by a brilliant pincer movement.

'We're three miles from the main body. We have to make sure our last precious supplies and guns get through this damn cold winters maw. Bloody buggering artillery,' Paget cursed, 'always the last. We have to wait for one lot to cross and then we blow the bridge north of the town. Then, we'll have to march like the devil up to where we expect to face the French.' He turned in the saddle to watch a dog run past them, barking madly as it disappeared into the throng of people. A redcoat was sat on a barrel drinking from a stone bottle while two companions were hassling a married couple who were trying to leave the town. 'The townsfolk that are our allies are coming with us, but most will stay. They seem to prefer the Jacobins. We're also leaving the wounded, those that can't be transported of course, to the mercies of the French.'

It was a terrible decision to leave men behind, but the French would look after them as would the British if it was the other way round. The weather had claimed many lives and most were exhausted and suffering from frost-bite, but the French would do their best to treat them.

'What about our allies, sir?' Hallam glanced at the ash that floated about them like the End of Days.

'Can't expect much from the Prussians or Austrians,' Paget muttered dismissively. 'No help whatsoever.'

'What about the Dutch?' Hallam had to shout, as the Inniskillings were being ordered to form up close by. Two of the men were fighting on the ground and, most bizarrely, no officer or NCO seemed to have the inclination to stop them.

Paget snorted. 'Might as well let their women fight instead,' he said sighing. 'No, they've buggered off, so we're on our own. We've got a battle to fight and ships to get to.'

'They will come, won't they, sir?' Hallam betrayed what every redcoat was thinking.

'Of course, Jack,' Paget scoffed at the notion that the ships wouldn't be there. It was unthinkable. No British army had been left behind. The Royal Navy was dependable. He looked up at the sky that was darkening as though all light was slowly being banished. 'We'll get home.'

'What's the name of the place we're marching to today, sir?'

'Grave.'

Hallam stared. 'How apt, sir,' he said drily.

Paget grunted at the irony. 'Probably not the way the locals say it,' he said tersely. 'I sincerely hope we can send the enemy to early ones, though. It'll be a desperate fight all right.'

And it would be too. The French would fight like fanatics while the British would fight because their lives depended on it.

At a place called Grave.

****

The 28th left Rotheheim in a terrible snowstorm.

They were the last regiment to leave the town. Two troops of cavalry: a Light Dragoon and a French émigré protected the rear-guard, but in the driving snow it was hard to see the man in the next file let alone if the enemy were near.

The wind brought snow and ice into the men's eyes causing them to curse and stumble. One man who had lost his boots a month before, and whose toes had all turned black, collapsed from exhaustion. His body instantly spotted white and as the wind howled across the fields the British cavalry passed him unnoticed and forgotten. Men sobbed and shuffled in the storm. They were benumbed with cold and bitterly hungry as no food or wine had been left for them at the town.

They passed frozen corpses lining the road, like markers showing the way to hell. They were humped grotesque shapes, like snow-covered barrows. Hallam stared at one. The man had been a redcoat and had been there for many days. His face was blackened by wind and half-buried in snow so that his grotesque face seemed to watch the men who marched past. Hallam's eyes flickered to another body and he almost wept at the sight.

21

In his long service career he had seen some terrible things. He'd seen men shredded into ribboned meat by canister shot, a friend decapitated by a roundshot and another die of a horrible wasting disease, but nothing had prepared him for this. The body was a young woman. Late teens. Her hair was copper-coloured and she resembled Isabel, for she had been strikingly good-looking in life. Her eyes were blessedly shut and her thin mouth closed. Her bodice was open, her breasts were exposed and the lower half of her was hidden under snow. Hallam bent over, not to gaze at her body, but because he couldn't make out what was lying next to her. He had to hold a hand to his eyes to shield them from the snow. Beside her, in a tight bundle and as though it had been tossed aside, was her child. Its little face was blue and its eyes were open. Hallam struggled to keep what little food he had in his stomach down.

'Nice tits,' said one of the redcoats who saw the woman.

'Eyes front!' Hallam turned on the man with a sudden fury. He stood and spoke to the rest of the company. 'If I so much as catch one of you bastards looking at her, you will be put on a charge!'

'Is that a..?' Stubbington started, but blanched.

'Yes,' Hallam said sombrely. 'Poor lass.'

Stubbington stood aghast. 'How did this happen? How?' he appealed.

Hallam could offer no reason. 'You best return to your post,' he could only think to say.

When the ensign had gone, Hallam wrenched a frozen saddlecloth from one of the horses to cover her waxen body. He tucked the baby underneath it and said a brief prayer, but because he was not a God-faring man, he couldn't recite much. When he finished, he stood for a while in solace. He shivered and pulled his scarf closer to his neck and mouth. Then, with nothing more to say, he gave the pale sour light behind a momentary look before walking on.

****

An hour later, they reached the bridge that crossed a swollen stream. It forked north and east. To the north, the road climbed to a thicket of birch trees, while to the east stood an old ruined mill that

22

shepherds sometimes used to shelter from the weather. The mill was deserted now.

The Slashers marched over the bridge to bar the road, and once they were in position they were ordered to halt. There were just the eight battalion companies, because the Light and Grenadiers had been sent on ahead with the 27th. The baggage, the regiment's equipment, and their wives and children had all gone on ahead too.

Hallam stamped his boots on the ground, breaking a virgin patch of snow. Like the rest of his men, he couldn't feel his toes. The companies were forbidden to gather wood to build fires because they would be leaving soon, which caused the men to grumble. He noticed one of his men kept looking over his shoulder.

'What's the matter, Shawford?'

The private licked his lips nervously. 'I was just thinking about the wife, sir.' He had married a thin girl who had given him a son, James, known as Little Jim. Rose Shawford was one of the handful of company wives that had followed their men in the campaign.

'Something wrong?' Hallam asked.

'There must be if he's thinking of his wife,' Tipton said, and the men laughed.

Even Shawford joined in, but his gap-toothed laughter died easily and the uneasiness returned quickly. 'Rose and Little Jim aren't well, sir. My son was awake all night with a dreadful cough and Rose ain't herself of late.'

'I'm sure they're going to be fine, Private,' Hallam replied. 'Your Rose is tougher than Sergeant Fox.' The laughter started and faded quickly again. Hallam understood the anxiety of missing, or fretting for a loved one. He shot the private a long confident grin and slapped him on the arm. 'Rose and your little boy will be fine. It's this damned country that's the cause of it. How many men have we lost to maladies?' He smiled. Shawford looked horrified. Hallam winced. 'That isn't what I meant.' He sighed, and then spoke slowly. 'What I mean is she's a strong woman and Little Jim will be as right as rain once we leave. It won't be long before we're on home soil.'

The private dipped his head. 'Thank you for your kind words, sir.'

'Not at all. And once we're at rest, you have my permission to spend the rest of the day with your family. I'll see to it that you assist Rose with your personal belongings too when the train leaves in the morning.'

'Thank you, sir. If it's all right with the captain?'

Hallam's eyes flicked to Clements, and then back to the private 'Don't you worry about that.'

Colonel Paget, along with Major Osborne, trotted over to the engineer who was making notes in a small leather-bound book. His black side-whiskers were coated with ice, which made him look older than his years. The wind plucked at their scarves and whistled about their muffled ears.

'Will it work in this weather?' Paget asked the engineer, who was called Munday.

'It should go bang for you,' Munday said irritably, as though his reply was to discourage further comment. There were two empty carts next to him, which had contained the gunpowder barrels. Their iron-rimmed wheels were rusted and spindles of ice hung from the axle.

The engineer was accompanied by half a dozen men from the Royal Military Artificers and Labourers, who were just as morose. A squat sergeant, who carried a small hatchet, hawked and spat over the stonework. The men had finished with the gunpowder that they had packed in the arches and would join the battalion on the journey north once the bridge was destroyed. The sergeant kicked one of the mules on; the empty cart squealed horribly along the road.

'I understand a gun got jammed here,' Paget said affably. He was trying to be pleasant to cover his anxieties. 'Luckily for us, they've managed to get unstuck. Or at least I assume they have.'

Munday just shrugged and said nothing.

A small wind brought a flurry of snow along the bridge and Paget swivelled his head to avoid getting any in his eyes. He turned to Osborne who offered him no support. Instead, the major stared up at the mill, and tapped a hard-boiled egg gently against the pommel of his sword.

'I wish I had some salt,' he said longingly as he pulled some of the brown shell away. 'A little sprinkle of salt would go down a treat.'

Stubbington slashed at some tall yellow stalks with his sword and then walked to where Hallam was standing behind the last file of men on the company's right flank. He saw tracks in the snow, little ones. Rabbit, he considered. He gazed expectantly at the thin, bare hedges, but could see nothing, and he rubbed his empty stomach. His coat was crusted with snow like the coats of the rest of the men.

'Where's our cavalry, sir?' he asked Hallam.

Hallam was just wondering that too. He explained how they would have to wait here until the horsemen were across the bridge, but how long would that be he wondered. The French vanguard would be cavalry too. They'd be just as cold and tired and neither side would have the advantage. Once the bridge was blown up, the enemy would have to find another way across. But all the same, he felt terribly exposed where they were, which added to the misery. It was like waiting for the hangman's noose.

It was an eerie place, Hallam thought. There was an abandoned round stone windmill to the east, the wooden sails creaking with the wind. Once or twice, a bird flapped in the trees, which caused the men to glance nervously over their shoulders. But other than that, he could only hear the slow trickle of water and the whistling wind.

'How long?' Paget said to Munday after a few minutes of silence. He was clearly becoming impatient with the wait, now shifting irritably in his saddle.

Just then a shout from Captain Richard Hussey Vivian's company alerted them to a single rider approaching from the dark tree line.

As the figure got closer, it became apparent that he was an officer of the Royal Artillery. He wore a black round hat with a huge black fur crest, a large crimson sash curled around his greatcoat and he wore white breeches with topped riding boots. A black scarf was wrapped around his face, which he lowered when he approached the officers on the bridge. Foaming white spittle flecked the horse's bit. He slowed his mount.

'Captain Francis Fyfield, sir,' he said, saluting. Fyfield had warm friendly eyes that betrayed an easy-going nature.

'Good afternoon, Captain,' Paget said cheerfully, pleased that he had someone else to talk to. 'What brings you back here?'

'I come to ask if you could help with a situation that has occurred beyond those trees,' Fyfied said, pointing a gloved hand up the crest. 'I'm in a dreadful quandary to be sure.'

'Go on, old boy,' Paget said as Osborne grunted in displeasure.

'Thank you, sir. One of my guns has broken a wheel. The driver did not see the verge in the road because of the snowfall and the drop broke its spokes. We're just waiting for a spare, but that could take one, maybe two hours, as the limbers were sent on. I wonder if you could send a few men to help my gun-team. They're exhausted from pulling the guns by hand. We've only got one horse left and the poor thing has got cow hocks.'

Paget wasn't sure what Fyfield meant by that and tried not to show it. 'How many guns do you have?'

'Only two now, sir,' Fyfield replied. 'Used to have three, but poor Lizzie cracked her barrel so we had to spike her at Rotheheim.'

'I see.' Paget paused for a second, before deciding that the British cavalry would not be far off and that they all had to march up the rise anyway once the bridge was destroyed. 'We will help you to be sure.'

'Thank you, sir,' Fyfield said.

'The first six battalion companies are to assist with the gun team, while the last two companies can wait with Munday until he has completed his task.'

Osborne instantly snorted with derision.

Paget twisted in the saddle. 'Something you wish to say, Major?'

Osborne had a tendency to question his decisions lately and Paget was getting fed up with the disrespect. More so, because this was in front of a lower ranking officer.

'I wouldn't have expected you to understand our predicament,' Osborne flashed him with a smile that showed no warmth. 'I would not split the regiment up. You've already lent the Light and Grenadiers for some damn foolish assignment. No more, I beg you. It would be seriously imprudent to do that, and I don't think a colonel, especially a newly commissioned one, should continue making reckless decisions without consulting his experienced deputy first.'

'I do not require schooling like some dull-witted child,' Paget said, his nostrils flaring. 'I understand the situation. I do not require your consideration.'

Osborne gave Paget a stern look. 'I implore you to consider my reasoning. I'm sure we can pull the regiment through this mess of a campaign with some dignity if we just allow some common sense.'

Paget said nothing for a moment. 'Reasoning, eh?' he replied distantly, as though he was replaying Osborne's insolence in his mind. He thought he could smell rum on the man's breath.

The major nodded emphatically. 'Reasoning indeed.'

Munday shifted uncomfortably below them. Fyfield was also embarrassed and looked across the river to the dilapidated mill as though he suddenly found it interesting.

'Very well, Osborne,' Paget said nodding. 'I'll leave you in command of the remaining companies whilst I take the rest of battalion up the hill. As an experienced and rational officer, you'll know what to do if the Crapauds show up.' Paget flashed him with a similar smile, then turned to Fyfield. 'Time to rescue your guns, Captain,' he said happily.

And with that, they both trotted away leaving Osborne sour-faced and Munday grinning.

****

When Munday was satisfied with the charge, he walked back towards the two companies; then, after a few paces, he cast a look over his shoulder and gave a sudden yell in warning.

French dragoons.

The green-coated cloaked horsemen came out of grey-sleet like vengeful wraiths seeking to claim a soul. The dragoons were cavalry excellent for reconnaissance, screening, pursuit and with their pale-as-ice swords, buff breeches and cloth-covered helmets, were part of the French vanguard.

The enemy had caught up with them.

'Company - make ready!' Hallam was the first officer to react.

'They are ours, you damned fool!' Clements shouted, typical rankness shaping his opinion.

'French bastards!' Private Hulse gave his opinion. A man on the flanks gasped at the shapes.

Clements put down his canteen. 'They-they can't be?' he said, distraught.

'They bloody well are,' Hallam said.

'Make ready your firelocks!' Fox bellowed at the men who were unsure and inactive.

The British were equipped with the 'Brown Bess', or Short Land Pattern musket that had a forty-two inch barrel, and a fifteen-inch triangular socket bayonet. Cold, hungry and bone-weary bodies were suddenly animated in unison. Rags were untied from locks, corks were unplugged from muzzles and the walnut musket stocks were brought straight up, perpendicular to the ground; the left hand on the swell of the stock, the right hand pulling the lock to full cock, and grasping the wrist of the firearm.

'By God, they are French,' Clements said in a strained voice.

'No one ever listens to me,' Hulse said miserably.

Munday tried to run, but the leading Frenchman was already on him. The hooves were thundering and the horse's eyes were white and he slashed down with his sword to split the engineer's skull in two. Blood misted the air crimson. The artificers were running, but one slipped on the ice and the horses ran over him as he attempted to get away. The sergeant pushed the others on and threw himself down on the snow just as a long sword sliced open his shoulder.

'Present!' Hallam ordered. Muskets went to shoulders.

'Present!' Clements copied with a bark. 'I give the goddamn orders here!' His contempt could not be made clearer.

'Aim low!' Hallam ignored Clements. He had tried to drum into the company the care needed when levelling a piece, particularly to the men new to the company who always aimed too high.

The dragoons, perhaps twenty of them, were crossing the span of the bridge. Their mounts had rags tied to their hooves for better footing in the ice and their huge lungs sent great jets of hot breath that steamed in the frigid air.

'Wait for it!' Hallam repeated for the few nervous men who might be tempted to pull their triggers too early.

One of the artificers tried to stop one of the mules from bolting up the hill and gripped the reins, but tripped and was dragged along the ice past the redcoats where one man laughed hysterically.

'Fire!' Clements barked.

'No!' Hallam countermanded, but it was too late.

Perhaps thirty muskets fired, the rest were damp and the range was too great. Clements had wasted the volley for none of the horsemen were hurt.

'Load!' Hallam ordered because the captain had seemingly forgotten what to do next. Hot gunpowder motes bit the inside of his nose.

Clements licked his dry lips. Vivian's company hadn't fired yet, but the dragoons would soon overrun the two companies. Better to save one than lose both. He looked back at the trees where Paget had taken the other companies. He reckoned that he could make it to the crest taking his company with him. It was better to fight on higher ground. 'Fall back!' he yelled, waving his sword towards the hill, spurring his horse violently. 'Fall back!'

'No!' Hallam grabbed the nearest man that tried to follow Clements. 'Stand your ground! Stand! Sergeant Fox!'

'Sir.'

'You may kill any man who moves without your permission!' Hallam ordered.

Fox grinned like a fed hound. 'It'll be a pleasure, sir.'

Hallam turned to Captain Vivian who nodded at him as though he approved of his unwavering ability. Vivian was a dandy, but he was also a good officer. 'Load, you bastards!' Hallam bellowed at the stragglers. They gazed awkwardly, then returned to their files where they were met with growls from those who had remained.

'Carry on, Lieutenant Hallam,' Vivian said, smiling. He turned back to his men. When the enemy were thirty yards away, he flicked his sword down. 'Fire!'

The company's front blossomed into smoke as the musket's fired. Vivian's timing was lethal and the leading dragoons were all killed in an instant. Bodies slid from saddles. Horses screamed and stumbled.

The rest of the dragoons swerved, but as Hallam's men brought muskets to shoulders most took their mounts away. A few stubborn ones, still charged, because the redcoats were in line and not in a defensive formation. Hallam ordered platoon fire and after the second volley the surviving horsemen had retreated back over the bridge.

Stubbington's face was drained of colour. 'What about the Captain, sir?'

Hallam was silent. He was just staring across the riverbank, where grotesque figures lurked and crouched in the sleet. Dismounted dragoons. He heard a shout from across the water and suddenly two dozen carbines flamed and three men from Vivian's company, who were the closest to the French, fell dead. One body slithered slowly down the ice leaving a ghastly trail of blood.

Clements returned, somehow finding his nerve. His usual surly face was now twisted in a mixture of fury, humiliation and terror. Hallam snubbed him. He was thinking. The bridge was still intact because Munday had not completed the task. The surviving artificers had joined the company and Hallam had an idea.

'His tinderbox,' the hatchet-armed sergeant said after Hallam quizzed him. 'He uses it to light the fuses.' His speech was like the hissing of a snake because he was missing his front teeth. 'It must be still on him,' he said, wincing as a colleague tried to staunch the blood pouring from the wound.

One of Vivian's Grenadiers was shot through the bowels and was dragged screaming back behind the line before the space was filled.

'Mister Stubbington,' Hallam said. 'I am going down to the bridge to light the bugger up.'

'Sir?'

'To light the fuse!' Hallam snapped at the ensign's lack of comprehension. 'It's the only bloody way to stop the French from crossing.' He purposely ignored Clements who had sheepishly joined Osborne behind Vivian's company. Hallam gazed at them. Useless cowardly bastards, the pair of them. He would look after the men himself as Clements didn't give a damn.

'Let me come, sir.'

'No, stay here with the company.'

'But, sir-' Stubbington went to object, but Hallam cut him short.

'Do as you're bloody told!' Hallam turned to his men. 'Company - fix bayonets!'

The men slotted the blades and he saw that Vivian's men were doing the same. It was the proper directive when threatened with cavalry so Hallam ordered it.

'Advance!' Hallam led them forward, the bayonet points glinting. He would get the men closer to the bridge to provide covering fire, but out of harm's way if there was a premature explosion.

The higher-pitched shots of carbines snapped at the redcoats and a man in the front rank gasped before collapsing onto his front. He did not move again. Another man was uttering a prayer over and over.

Hallam knew there wasn't much time. In a few minutes, the French could launch a larger attack and the long straight swords would chop and hack, and moustached faces beneath brass peaks would grin and laugh at the slaughter.

'Halt!' Hallam saw that Vivian had understood what he was doing and so his company edged closer to the dark swollen river. A man stepped away and Hallam pushed him back into his rank. 'Take over, Mister Stubbington! Sergeant Fox!'

'Sir!'

'Keep him alive,' Hallam jerked his head at the ensign and Fox grinned. Then, Hallam took a deep breath and sprinted down the snow that reached the tops of his boots.

'Platoon fire!' Fox shouted.

The splintering noise of sustained musket fire hammered towards the French, the echoes pounding up the slope to the tree line.

'Thank you, Sergeant Fox,' said Stubbington. 'I'll take it from here.'

'Very good, sir.'

Hallam threaded through the French bodies and jumped a horse that was lying on its side, legs jerking. A bullet fluttered past him. He drew his sword. It was an old one that he had been given as a gift from his friend and mentor Captain George Milsum who had bequeathed him the sword on his deathbed. Milsum had carried the sword as an ensign at the capture of Quebec in the Seven Years' War. It was an old sword, ugly, straight-bladed and brutal, yet had a bluish tint and sparkled as thought it had just been crafted, and he would not go into battle without it.

Hallam slipped on the ice and from a puddle of blood that oozed thickly from a dying horse. His hat fell from his head and a bullet clanged on his scabbard. He could see horsemen off across to the west on the road, and dismounted dragoons who were stooping over frozen hedgerows, the river banks and across the lichen covered stonework of the bridge. He saw the long fuse line and then he saw Munday, his head was nearly cloven in two. Hallam could see brain amongst the glistening gore. There were dragoons on this side of the river and the nearest one saw him first.

Hallam slashed across his body to parry the attack, using the strongest lower third of the blade, nearest the hilt known as the forte. The blades rang like a bell. The Frenchman was gritting his teeth as his blade scraped down the steel to be stopped by Hallam's sword guard. Hallam threw off the blade and then punched forward with his cross-guard to shatter the Frenchman's front teeth and split his lips. Blood and splintered bone erupted from his ruined mouth as he fell backwards. The second dragoon, whose shot had struck Hallam's scabbard, now charged at him, swinging his sword and yelling as though he was gripped in terror. Hallam desperately brought up his sword and the blades crashed against each other. His assailant slipped, tried to regain his balance, but Hallam used it to his advantage and he disentangled his sword to thrust up between the Frenchman's ribs. He gave Hallam a look of surprise before he died. The injured dragoon, blood trickling down his chin, got to his knees and Hallam chopped down with his sword and the blade hit the side of the man's cloth-covered helmet, making a clanging sound, and ripping the canvas away to reveal a flash of brass.

The third dragoon was more cautious and took time to aim his carbine at Hallam's trunk. He pulled the trigger. The hammer went forward and there was a dull click. Nothing happened. The powder was damp and the dragoon swore for the weapon being useless. He dropped the carbine and fumbled for his sword, which hung from its wrist strap. He was a large man, clumsy with big hands and thick fingers and couldn't bring the sword up in time before Hallam kicked him massively between the legs. The Frenchman gave an odd high-pitched wail before clutching at his groin, falling sideways and rolling on the ground in agony.

Hallam saw more shapes from the road and more carbine fire snapped at him. Bullets whistled overhead and smacked into the stonework, showering him and the three dragoons with sparks and stone chippings. But none of the enemy approached. He bent down and went through Munday's heavy coat, until his hand touched something metallic in one of the pockets: the tinderbox.

Hallam heard French voices and he looked up. A handful of dragoons were now running towards him. He jerked aside from a puff of smoke and a bullet fanned the air by his ear. But then an explosion of musketry to his left threw the dragoons down in an instant. He could just make out Stubbington in the musket smoke and he smiled. The ensign appeared to be in control. *Good boy*, Hallam said to himself, *good boy*.

He opened the tin case and within was the fire-steel, charcloth and a piece of chipped flint. Good, that was everything he needed. He shortened the slow match by ripping it apart by the main charge, then struck the flint on the ring of steel. A tiny spark flew, but died in the wind. He tried again and the same thing happened. A bullet smacked into the arch above his head, but he didn't look up. He bent closer to the slow match. The spark caught the linen on the third attempt, but it went out. He tried a fourth time and he blew on it until the tinder flared up. A ghost of a smile lit his eyes when he put the flame to the fuse and the powder fizzed and smoked. One of the dragoons groaned in pain and Hallam hit him hard in the belly.

He could hear horses. Out of the greyness, the French were launching a larger mounted assault, perhaps because they had brought reinforcements. The bridge had to be destroyed now! Another crackle of musketry and Vivian's men threw down three dragoons, but it was the charging horsemen that worried Hallam. The fuse was still fizzing, but it was taking too damn long. The enemy were charging. Hallam heard a French officer screaming at his men. The fuse burned fiercely. He only had seconds. He turned and ran for dear life.

'Fire!' Vivian, resplendent in his fine uniform, shouted. Another volley tore into the French and a dragoon, hit, momentarily staggered, and then fell into the water. It swirled red.

'Back!' Hallam shouted desperately. 'Get back!'

Behind him, the mounted dragoons galloped past the charge, the hooves clattered on the ice and stone. One man saw the smoke and dismounted. He lifted one boot to stamp out the fuse.

But he was too late.

The fuse puffed once more and then the world exploded.

The fizzing, sparking fuse ate into Munday's charge and the powder ignited. Great flickering tongues of flame leapt into the air, where the smoke turned it instantly black.

Hallam threw himself onto the ground at the moment of the explosion. He was dazed by the overwhelming, ear-splitting detonation. He stood, slipped, and staggered towards the redcoats. Great chunks of stone and debris smashed down onto the snow, ice and water. Hallam slipped once more, but hands picked him up and steadied him.

It was Sergeant Fox. His mouth was open, but Hallam could not hear him.

'What?' he said, and rubbed his ears. The sound was dull at first, hardly audible, and then it was replaced with a high-pitched ringing.

'Are you all right, sir?' Fox was saying.

Hallam groaned. 'Yes,' he shouted.

The redcoats were cheering. Hallam turned to see the destruction that he had caused. The bridge was completely gone. The enemy horseman had been obliterated and the few survivors retreated dazed, confused and beaten. The bridge was nothing but a blackened stump. He had done it.

'Well done, sir!' Stubbington was almost jumping in joy. 'You're a damned hero!'

'Jesus, my ears.'

Vivian came over and slapped Hallam's back. Osborne was ignoring him, and was speaking to Paget's adjutant who had come down to investigate the commotion.

'You're a reckless bastard, Lieutenant,' a voice spoke from behind. Hallam turned. Clements gave a begrudging smile, which was more like a grimace.

'Congratulations, Mister Stubbington,' Hallam said, whilst looking directly at Clements. His voice was still loud. 'You kept your nerve and you never faltered. The men will respect you for that. You're now a far better officer than some I can think of.'

Clements looked as though he had been struck. His cheeks twitched violently at the contemptuous insolence. He was unable do anything, because he knew he had panicked, and shaking with vehemence, he let Hallam walk away, the hero of the hour.

****

Mr Thomas Carew, the 28th's quartermaster wanted to get moving.

The battalion, along with the rest of the 6th Brigade, was not due to set out until nine o'clock, but Carew had been marshalling the baggage train two hours before dawn in the hope that they would be ready at least an hour before nine. This was because the bullocks plodded and the baggage and transport always held up the main column. Carew wanted to change that. Colonel Paget had been furious with the last few days trundling pace and Carew wanted to show him how good a job he could do. It was going well until the damned children got in the way; weaving in and out of the bullocks, getting tangled in the chains and hanging from the carts to see who could last the longest before falling. At first, Carew threatened them with the whip, but begrudgingly saw the funny side and let himself warm to the laughter of playing children.

It was then that there were shouts coming from the wives and Carew signalled the train to stop. He was furious. He suspected a child had yanked boxes off the carts.

'What's going on here?' he yelled.

'Mrs Shawford and Little Jim are missing, Mr Carew,' answered one of the wives. 'They ain't been seen this morning.'

'I thought I saw her at the rear?'

'She ain't there!' Another wife said. A young baby fed at her breast.

Carew scratched his head. He could feel his entire scalp move from the lice. 'Where's Private Shawford? I thought he was helping you lot pack your things?' A couple of the company's married men had been allowed to help their wives and friends with the move. The woman was busy feeding her child. Carew swore. 'So has the private and his wife absconded from the army?'

'No,' the woman said and yelped as the baby bit her nipple. 'You little sod. You're just like your bleeding father.'

Carew, frustrated, ignored her and went down the line to inspect the carts himself.

Fifteen minutes went by.

The train was still stationary and a company officer came up to Carew. It was Lieutenant Hallam.

'What's the hold up, Tom? The colonel's not very happy. Rumour has it that Major-General Cathcart is on his way here.' Cathcart commanded the brigade and was a stern man with little time for incompetence.

Carew looked worried. 'Oh, dear God!' Then he noticed Hallam grinning and knew he was being teased. 'Jack, don't play any more games with me. My heart won't take it. Private Shawford is in your company, is he not?'

'He is. What's he done?'

'Well, he ain't here and his wife ain't here either.'

Hallam shot Carew a serious glance. 'I allowed him to spend some time with his wife as she's been unwell. Have you seen them this morning?'

'No, Jack, I haven't. What am I to do now?'

Shawford was a reliable soldier and one Hallam considered would never desert his post. There must be some misunderstanding. Some miscommunication. The usual army calamities.

'I'll find them,' Hallam said, gaping up and down the baggage train. 'You get going, Tom.'

He walked down the train until his curiosity was satisfied. A couple of women were dressed in heavy shawls and had their pinched faces drawn up, so he had to ask them to drop their garments just to be sure. They weren't Rose Shawford. One of them was singing a mournful tune that pricked the hairs on the back of his neck. He returned to his company.

He accosted Stubbington who was trying not to get in the way of Clements horse.

'He's in his file, sir,' the ensign said. 'All present and correct.'

Hallam frowned, feeling that he had wasted his time, and strode over to the private who was indeed in his file.

'Why in God's name are you here? I gave you permission to help your wife this morning.'

The private looked aggrieved. 'You did that, sir. Except that the captain found out and ordered me back here.'

'He what?' Hallam said aghast. He turned to gawk at Clements, eyes tightened. He didn't wait for the private to answer him and walked to the captain's side. 'What's this I hear about Private Shawford?' he said, unable to curb his anger. 'I gave him permission to be with his sick wife.'

Clements ignored Hallam for a moment, pursed his lips and then glared at him. 'You gave an order that was not permitted, Lieutenant. An order that is not given by me is thus not official. For that insolence, Private Shawford will be punished for deserting his post.'

'You can't do that,' Hallam growled.

Clements laughed at his reaction. 'Of course I can. I'm the captain of this company, and I'll damn well do what I like. I've thought about bringing back picquetting,' he said, smiling widely with satisfaction.

Hallam glowered at the thought of the old punishment of making a wrong-doer stand bare foot for a length of time on a tent-peg being brought back.

'Or perhaps I'll simply have the scoundrel flogged?' Clements said it as though he was questioning himself. 'Nothing like a flogging to instil discipline where it's needed.'

'You'll do no such thing,' Hallam vented, before walking back to the unfortunate private. 'I'm sorry to say that Rose and Little Jim are missing,' he said quietly so that Clements could not hear. 'Quartermaster Carew informed me. I checked and I couldn't see them either.'

The old soldier seemed to shudder. 'What?'

37

'Don't worry,' Hallam said calmly. 'We're not going to abandon them.'

'What are you going to do, sir?'

'I'm going to get help,' Hallam replied, before disappearing.

****

Twenty minutes later, and against Clements' wishes, Sergeant Fox, Privates' Shawford, Hulse, Tipton and Phelps were called out of the retreating line by Major Osborne. They were told to report to Hallam at the double, before leaving their packs behind with the rest of the baggage.

'Ready your firelocks,' Hallam grinned when they found him at the rear of the battalion with the bandsmen.

'Sir?' Fox, knowing how to deal with eccentric officers had perfected every answer possible, but this request and situation was new to him.

'Do as you bloody told, Sergeant,' Hallam checked his pistol was loaded. When the men were ready, he explained. 'I've got some news,' he spoke to Shawford. 'Your wife and son were seen on the edge of that wood,' he pointed to the smear of trees to the south. 'One of the wives of the 27th saw a mother and son match their description. Rose was wearing her dark-red shawl, was she not?'

'Yes,' Shawford said, frowning. 'What would Rose be doing there?'

'Collecting firewood?' Hulse suggested. He had lost his round hat and instead wore a woollen forage cap that was a damp shapeless mass.

Hallam brought out his fob watch to check the time. 'Perhaps your son ran in there and Mrs Shawford duly followed him?'

The private glowered. 'The little bugger,' he said. 'I'll tan his hide for the trouble he's caused.' Everyone present knew that he would not do such a thing, because he doted on the boy.

'It's eleven o'clock,' Hallam said. 'Let's find them and bring them back before it gets dark.'

They jogged down the road. Their bayonets, cartridges and whatever foodstuffs they had in their haversacks bounced with each footfall.

Phelps wore two sack cloths over his jacket, because he had not been issued with a greatcoat. It made his body look ungainly. 'Any Frenchie bastards hereabouts, sir?' he asked.

'That's why the lieutenant ordered loaded weapons,' Fox answered, as though he was dealing with a difficult child.

Hallam scanned the trees ahead. The wind whipped cold. 'Our outlying picquets are a quarter of a mile away and we have the cavalry behind us protecting our arses.' The small detachment of men laughed derisively as was accustomed to the infantryman's usual scorn for their mounted comrades.

They jumped a frozen dike; Phelps only just managed to avoid tumbling into it. They ran on across a snowy field that had turned to slush from the rains. Tipton slipped, but kept his balance, and as every man held their muskets by the trail, no triggers were pulled and thus exposing their position.

'Here are some prints!' Hulse exclaimed.

Hallam studied the marks on the ground. Two sets. One definitely belonged to a child.

'This is where they went,' Hallam said with a smile. 'We'll soon find them.'

'How did you allow us to come on this special task, sir?' Shawford asked as they entered the woodland. It was eerily silent.

'I spoke to the colonel,' Hallam confirmed with a wink. 'I told him everything.'

Shawford let his eyes come accustomed to the darkness. 'The captain told me that I would be punished for leaving my post.'

'Like I said,' Hallam crept forward, free hand pulling away low branches from his unshaven face. 'I spoke to the colonel. The captain won't be doing anything.'

'Thank you, sir.' The private's relief was heartfelt.

Their boots crunched on snow as they hunched underneath boughs and threaded past thick bellied trees. Mistletoe dotted the knotted limbs. They couldn't see any footprints, but they followed the path into the heart of the shadowy wood.

'If we see a deer,' Tipton asked, 'are we allowed to shoot it, sir?'

'After we've made sure that it isn't Mrs Shawford, Little Jim, or any French bastards wandering about,' Hallam replied.

There was a sliver of water, black like a huge spill of ink upon the snow. Hallam saw something on its surface. It was a dog, swollen and hewn. Someone had killed it many days ago and tossed the corpse into the stream.

A woman screamed from somewhere in the trees, and immediately a great wave of fear and horror swept over the redcoats.

'Rose!' Shawford hurried forward.

'Rags off,' Fox ordered, and the men removed the strips of cloth tied around the musket locks.

'And fix bayonets,' Hallam added.

The track turned to thick mud, and beyond a tangle of brushwood that half-covered the track, was a farm. Its walls were coated in mould, the roof was dark with moss and rot. There was nobody outside, so the sound must have come from inside the farm.

'Smoke,' Hulse said, jutting his chin to the blue-grey covering amongst the dark branches.

'I'll find out who's inside. Wait here and keep alert!' Hallam rasped. He skirted the main path to skulk towards one of the shuttered windows on the building's eastern wall. There was a crack in the wood and he gently inched closer to peer inside.

There was a hearth-fire with a pot bubbling away and a battered table made of a length of wood over two pieces of cut timber. A small ham hung from the rafters, away from the rats and mice. He couldn't see anyone but there was a murmur of voices. Hallam leaned in even closer and a young boy with hair the colour of straw saw the movement to stare. It was Little Jim. Thank God, the child was safe. Snot hung from his nose and he was pale. Hallam put a finger to his lips, but the boy, not even four, did not understand, and just gaped innocently back.

Movement near the window. A man wearing a blue jacket took up a stone bottle and wiped his long flowing moustache afterwards. His hair was shoulder-length, falling unruly over the red collar of his jacket. Tied around his neck was a filthy red neckerchief. A woman moaned and the man grinned with tobacco stained teeth at the sound.

Laughter and French voices. The woman whimpered and Little Jim turned to watch unseen figures. His eyes glistened and his bottom lip dropped. The woman began to plead and Hallam instinctively growled.

The Frenchman, hearing the noise, pushed the shutter open and the pistol's cold muzzle pressed against his forehead.

Hallam watched the man's eyes narrow and then widen, before his mouth opened. Whatever he intended to shout was never heard, because the ball smashed through his skull to erupt in a bloody spray as it exited the back of the Frenchman's head.

There was a brief moment of silence.

'28th!' Hallam shouted, as he stepped back against the wall. 'Make ready!'

French shouts dizzied the air and the woman sobbed.

Before he had shot the man through the head, Hallam had seen a half dozen figures in the farm's murky interior. Eyes and faces tinted orange from the flame light and there was the unmistakable image of Mrs Shawford. She was half-dressed and lying down. Whatever the French were doing to her, Hallam could only guess with disgust.

There was no time to load the pistol again, so Hallam tucked it into his sash, and dragged his sword free. His men were crouched where he had left them, their coats just visible in the cold dank undergrowth.

The shutters to the front opened with a loud thud. Hallam saw two muskets appear at the window. A musket fired and Hallam knew one of his men had taken the shot. He knew Fox would be berating the private, but his concern was for Private Shawford, who had sprung up to charge the farm. The French had an easy target.

Hallam rushed towards the window, boots slipping in the mud, and reached out to grab the nearest enemy musket. He drove it forward onto the next one as triggers were pulled to send stabs of flame and smoke into the air. The proximity of the discharge was loud in his ears, but the shots had gone wide. Hallam twisted back and thrust his sword into the open space and felt the honed blade bite into flesh. He yanked it back and side-stepped as another musket crashed to send the racing ball high into the scrub.

41

'They're both inside!' Hallam wanted to warn his men. They were all rising.

The door opened abruptly. A tall Frenchman, wearing a blue jacket with red epaulettes and a bicorn with a drooping red horsehair plume, stepped outside hefting a bayonet-tipped musket. Shawford screamed as he charged. The enemy lowered his musket, weak sunlight caught on the long blade. For a heartbeat, Hallam thought the private would impale himself.

'Bloody French bastard!' Shawford snarled, and jerked his trigger. The bullet caught the Frenchman in the gullet and blew out through the back of his spine. The body dropped like a stone in water.

Another enemy emerged. This one wore a long, stained coat and cavalry overalls. The man flourished a straight-bladed sword, but Shawford reversed his musket and swung it with incredible force. The heavy stock collided with the side of the man's face with a sickening crack that sent him sprawling into the mud. Two more Frenchmen dashed out of the farm. The first brandished a large horse-pistol and Shawford brought his musket back to its correct position and rammed the blackened muzzle into the man's Adam's apple with the force of a sledgehammer. The enemy staggered, choking and Hallam's sword slashed left-to-right across his belly, sending coils of guts spilling and steaming onto the ground. The other screamed like a madman, swinging a two-handed axe. Shawford ducked, the blade knocked off his mildewed round-hat, and he ran inside the farm. Fox slashed the air with his bayonet and the enemy rushed forth his broad blade to parry the steel. The sergeant brought his blade up and the Frenchman chopped down to meet it, twisted as he anticipated Fox's next attack, but Hulse's bayonet ripped into his flank. The Frenchman screamed. Fox grunted as he stabbed his blade into the man's belly, who then collapsed, momentarily trapping both weapons with his dying body.

Hallam heard sobbing as he entered the farmhouse. Shawford was dressing Rose and Little Jim was crying. Hallam soothed the boy and picked him up.

'There, there, my love,' Shawford was saying over and over. 'No need to worry. I'm here now.' He heard his son and reached over

42

and took him from Hallam. Squeezing the boy tight, the old soldier could not control his emotions. He grasped Rose and the family cried and hugged each other. Hallam decided to leave them to it and then, out of the corner of his eye, noticed a seated figure next the hearth. The Frenchman grinned at Hallam's surprise with crooked black teeth. He looked relatively unhurt, but a swelling on his cheek revealed that Shawford had struck him.

Hallam stepped outside to check on his men who were already going through the enemy's pockets, feeling for hidden coins in the seams of coats. Haversacks and pouches torn off, some of the contents scattered about. The wounded man wearing the overalls had been bayoneted.

'They appear to be from different battalions, sir,' Fox was brusque, because he had been caught plundering and was embarrassed.

If Hallam was offended, then he didn't show it. 'Deserters?' His eyes fell upon the ragged uniforms.

'A motley collection of brigands, sir,' Hulse said, counting the coins, which they would share out.

'I suspect that this rabble had been hiding here for some time,' Fox said, gazing around. 'Quite a secluded spot for this den of thieves.'

' "The robbed that smiles steals something from the thief",' Hulse said to no one in particular.

'What are you going on about, Private?' Fox said, bewildered.

Hulse pointed and the men turned to the doorway. 'Othello,' he said.

Shawford, despite his wife's terrible distress, and the tears that glistened on his dark cheeks, beamed. 'Thank you,' his voiced wobbled. 'Thank you, for saving my family.'

'Think nothing of it,' Hallam said, pleased that they had found Mrs Shawford and the boy in one piece, despite the dreadful ordeal. Rose was white and sweating, tell-tale signs of the illness she was suffering from. She wiped the snot from her son's nose with a cloth. Hallam went to add that they should return to the regiment when a shape moved beyond the farmhouse.

A musket banged and Private Phelps spun backwards dead with a bullet in his heart.

Hallam saw sinister-looking men coming from the brush. 'Get in here, now!' he gestured at the farm.

More muskets exploded, but the redcoats managed to make it clear through the door without injury.

'Jesus!' Tipton said.

'More of the bastards!' Hulse ran to the farthest window through to the sleeping quarters that stank of decay and stale urine. The glass had a crack running up the filthy pane, but the private could see men crouch outside.

'How many do you see, Hulse?' Hallam called as he and Shawford pushed a heavy chest to the door and pulled the remnants of a barrel on top to fortify the entrance. Little Jim was crying and Shawford took his son in his arms, brought out a little soldier carved out of wood and let the boy play with it. Rose's face was unreadable.

'I count eight, sir.'

'Are there any other weapons in here?' Hallam said, wanting to keep the men busy.

'Jesus,' Tipton was saying over and over.

'Private Tipton, count to five and report,' Hallam ordered him.

The private wiped his face, chest heaving and belly squirming with nerves. 'Two Frenchie muskets, and two dead 'un's in here, sir. One of them stinks like a latrine.'

'What are we to do with this one, sir?' Fox asked of the bruised Frenchman. He brought out his sharpening stone and ran it expertly up his bayonet, revelling in the lethal zing the motion produced.

Hallam was loading his pistol. 'I don't know yet.'

The Frenchman fingered a chain around his neck and started to laugh.

'What's funny, you Crapaud bastard?' Hallam asked.

The enemy wiped saliva from his chin, which had dribbled out of his foul-looking mouth. 'You're going to let me go,' he replied in perfect English.

Hallam finished ramming the charge home and slotted the ramrod back in the rings beneath the barrel. 'You're not going anywhere.'

'May I have your name?'

'It's Lieutenant Hallam to you.'

The Frenchman's expression changed from absolute hilarity to grave solemnity in an instant. 'My name is Tristan Benoit. My father named me Tristan after the famous knight of King Arthur.' Benoit chuckled. 'He was such a romantic. I hated it as a boy, but I read *Le Morte d'Arthur* and I grew to love it. Have you read the book? No? I have had my own adventures. Like the chivalrous knight of the stories. Some worthy, most not,' he said, falling into laughter again. 'I am a *capitaine* in the -'

'You're a goddamn disgrace, that's what you are!' Hallam interrupted nastily. He was angered by the man's self-absorbance and cocksure bloody demeanour.

'I am a *capitaine-*' Benoit said stubbornly, but was cut off again.

'Deserters, murderers and... ' Hallam paused to choose the correct word, 'defilers of women, have no rank!' He caught the Frenchman's gaze and held it. 'You may command the scum out there, but you have no military authority, or influence here.'

Benoit breathed heavily, the red swelling on his cheek looked pulpy. 'My men will kill all of you. The only way to stop that is for you to let me go.'

Hallam watched him, hands fingering the loaded pistol. He could feel the heat of the fire begin to warm his bones, and despite the situation, it felt damned good. 'And then what? What happens if I let you go?'

Benoit showed his rotten teeth again. 'We will simply walk away. Leave you.'

'Walk away,' Hallam copied dubiously. Eyes still on the Frenchman he spoke to his men. 'Hulse! What are the bastards doing?'

'Just waiting, sir.'

'Tipton?'

'Same here, sir.'

Benoit looked about the room. 'There is nothing here for us anymore. We intended to move away before the snow's came, but it was early. So we stayed. It's been two months.'

'No wonder this place smells like a shit hole. What have you been doing all this time?'

The Frenchman shrugged. 'Hunting and robbing.'

Hallam laughed contemptuously. 'What an honourable man you are. You have no virtues of a knight.'

Benoit coughed as though his lungs were coming loose. 'I don't care what you think of me, or my men. We have been through hell. Hell, I tell you. I have seen terrible things. Things that would make an ordinary man piss his breeches at and scream until the surgeon would have to cut out his tongue to quieten him.' He gazed at the flames. 'I was at Jemappes. You heard of that?'

'No.'

'We defeated the Austrians and took Brussels,' Benoit said proudly. 'I lost many friends in that battle. Good men. They were heroes of the Revolution. I was wounded badly by cannon fire. I lay there in the day, unable to get up, as the battle raged. I fell unconscious. I woke in the night to find black creatures stripping the wounded of their possessions and in most cases, their lives. They missed me and I managed, despite the agony, to drag myself away and was found and taken to the hospital.'

'Is that when you deserted?' Hallam couldn't help but needle the man.

Benoit paused to consider the reply. 'My leg was terribly damaged, but I was spared the surgeon's knife. I was part of the garrison that stayed here, but after we lost hold of this country, I found myself uninterested in the army. I drifted away to join others. I've been in command for six months. I'm a good man-'

'Piss off,' Hallam said.

'I am a good man!' The Frenchman looked outraged.

'That,' Hallam said, 'from a man who has murdered, robbed and raped, is rich. Don't tell me that you wanted to do good things, but instead ended up doing bad things.'

Benoit did not answer.

Outside a voice called out.

'Your sweethearts are missing you,' Hallam mocked.

'They are asking if I am alive.'

'You can tell them you live.'

Benoit sighed. 'They will not be happy until I am free. Just let me go, and I'll give you my word that we'll leave in peace.'

46

Hallam leaned in closer to him, trying not to let the stink of the man's fetid breath affect him. 'How many men do you lead?'

Benoit pursed his lips. 'There were thirty of us at dawn.'

Hallam laughed. 'You lying bastard. I don't think so. There are eight out there, maybe another two concealed. At best you have ten men remaining. And you want me to lead my men, a woman and a child out there for you to shoot us in the back.'

'I give you my word that we will not do that,' Benoit said.

Little Jim, shivering, said something to his father and the Frenchman turned to look at the boy.

Hallam reached forward and struck Benoit hard across the face. The sudden attack startled everyone. 'If you look at him, or Mrs Shawford again,' he said menacingly, 'I'll cut your goddamn throat.'

Benoit looked defiant for a moment, but then understood the threat was real. 'As I said, we have been through hell.'

'So has every soldier of this damned campaign!' Hallam exploded. 'You think because you survived a battle and saw the horror of what it brings entitles you to a life of crime? No, sir, it does not! That is a piss poor excuse. Now you're going to sit there with your mouth shut while I talk to your men.'

'They don't speak English.'

Hallam glared at the man. 'Then it will be quick.'

He walked over to where Hulse watched from the window and studied the men outside. He counted eight. They were crouched low and were hard-faced. One man had an eye-patch and another wore an Austrian uniform, and all had muskets.

'They have stripped poor Phelps of his firelock and cartridges, sir,' Hulse said in a quiet voice. 'They were laughing.'

Hallam growled. He made sure Hulse was loaded before checking Tipton.

'They come any closer and I'll shoot them, sir,' the boy tried to sound confident.

'That's what you're paid to do, Private,' Hallam said. Tipton looked at him, saw the smirk on his lieutenant's face and grinned back.

'Very good, sir.'

Hallam made a mental note. They had four of their own muskets, the two French and his pistol. He checked the Frenchman he had shot through the window to find a clasp knife and a smaller pistol tucked into his belt. He went about loading the French 1777 Charleville musket when Rose came over and snatched a musket from his hands.

'Mrs Shawford-'

'I can load a musket, Lieutenant Hallam,' she said belligerently. She was pallid and sweat beaded her forehead and top lip. 'Even a Frenchie one.'

Hallam thought better than to disagree and left her to it. He walked over to her husband. 'Does she know what she's doing?' he asked. 'She might break the damn thing.'

Shawford grinned. 'She can do it, sir. She won't give up. Stubborn like her ma. She'll do it until she breaks it. Or breaks a nail. And if she breaks a nail, then she'll definitely break it.'

Hallam turned when the musket cocked. Rose shot him a look of triumph. 'Thank you, Mrs Shawford,' he said, trying not to smile. She reached for the second gun. 'I think we have another volunteer, lads,' he said.

The men cheered, which provoked a hail of musketry from outside. Little Jim started to cry again, but Shawford hushed the boy.

'Do not return fire!' Hallam barked. The balls had hit the roof and walls. 'They're just trying to scare us.'

And they're doing a grand job of it, he mused. Hallam's eyes skimmed across to his men to gauge their reaction. Both Hulse and Tipton were trying not to let the threat upset them. Fox was his usual glowering self. Shawford's tough exterior was weakening with every minute of being trapped here with his abused, ill wife and son. He was fearful of what might befall them and Hallam sympathised. Benoit lapsed into silence, which was good. Hallam didn't want to hear him talk anymore; however, he half-wondered whether the Frenchman's offer was genuine or not. Could he be trusted? Would they really be allowed to leave without being attacked? It was pulling his thoughts like a loose thread. But he considered that having Fox and Shawford with him was enough to see they had the advantage. Besides, they were warming up whilst the enemy outside must be getting colder. They would stay here tonight and break out in the early hours when the enemy was frozen. A quick dash to safety against cold and tired men. That would work. They couldn't stay here long, otherwise they might run into the French vanguard. It was risky, but there was little choice. Nonetheless, Hallam felt confident of success.

A voice called from outside and Hallam was tempted to ignore it, but Hulse called him over.

'Bugger's speaking English, sir.'

Hallam considered Benoit a liar and everything he said was a game of deceit. He snorted his disdain. 'What did he say?'

'Sounded like he wanted to talk,' Hulse said.

Hallam watched the man with the eye-patch walk closer. His hands were up and he was unarmed.

Hallam thought for a second. 'I'm going to open the door, but you keep your eyes on these bastards. If any one of them moves you shout out.'

'I will, sir.'

He told Tipton the same and moved back to the door. Rose and Little Jim moved into a little room, barely big enough for a cupboard and Hallam guessed this was the pantry. Two stone jars were broken on the floor and he thought he could smell the tang of pickled foodstuffs for an instant.

'Watch that bastard,' Hallam said to Fox, as he moved the chest aside. The door creaked open.

The deserter calmly walked to the farmhouse, stopping about three feet away. He studied Hallam's partially shadowed face for weakness and was surprised to see none. For months, the group had raided local villages; stealing food, killing the menfolk and raping the women. They had surprised a British cavalry detachment, which had used a stable a mile to the west. The horsemen had not thought to check the woods for enemies, and Benoit's men had bayoneted them in their sleep. They had taken the horses, but a few of Benoit's men had ridden off in search of other employment, leaving four horses. The beasts had been eaten as the cold weather came in and food became harder to come by. No one searched for them and their confidence grew. On one occasion, they had captured a Hanoverian

49

messenger, sent to bring a British brigade into the nearest town, but they killed him. Benoit's men remained untouched and untroubled, and free to continue their criminalities.

'You are an officer, *oui?*' the deserter enquired. He was confident and looked as though he had years of military experience.

'I am.' Hallam looked the man up and down too. His bicorn was frayed and without a plume and cockade. He had a goat skin pack, a knife in a brown leather sheath at his hip and his long coat hung down to his knees. Hallam noticed his boots were held together with twine.

The man's one eye flickered to the windows. '*Capitaine* Benoit is inside?'

'Yes.'

'May I see him?'

'No,' Hallam said laconically. Behind him, the walls glowed orange from the fire.

The Frenchman shrugged. 'I would like to speak to him.'

Hallam was tempted to deny him, but considered speaking through the door would be the lesser of evils. 'Step forward and speak only in English.'

The deserter attempted to object. 'My English is not so good.'

'I think it is good enough,' Hallam said. 'Now step forward and speak, or bugger off.'

The Frenchman frowned in disagreement; cast a look over his shoulder, then deciding it was futile to stand his ground, walked towards the door.

Hallam did not see if the man had made a signal to the men, but considered the notion. As the deserter stepped up to the door, he could smell decay, sweat and smoke emanating from his clothes.

'May I see him please?' The deserter tried to see past Hallam's frame.

'I said no,' Hallam replied firmly.

The Frenchman licked his chapped lips. The skin on his face was stretched tight over wide cheek bones, and his blood-shot eyes hung with thick lids. '*Mon Capitaine.*'

There was silence.

'Speak up,' Hallam ordered the captive without turning around.

'I am here, Sas,' Benoit said.

Sas did not clearly know what to do. He scratched his face with dirty nails. 'Sir?'

Benoit hesitated as if mulling over what he might say next, and drew breath to speak. 'Wait for me. I shall be free soon.'

'I will, *mon Capitaine.*'

'You and I have been friends for a long time, *non?*'

Sas smiled. '*Oui.*'

'You were at my side at Jemappes,' Benoit said. 'Remember the dawn light that morning?'

'I do. It was beautiful.'

Benoit sounded wistful. 'It was September, wasn't it? Crisp evening's with beautiful sunrises. And the battle started as the sun was still climbing. How many times did we attack?'

'I lost count, sir.'

Benoit chuckled. 'And we rallied at midday. Remember what we did then?'

A smile spread on Sas's lips. He patted his chest. '*Oui.*'

'Then go now, *mon ami,*' Benoit ordered. 'Go and wait for me.'

Sas went to move but Hallam leaned in closer to the door. 'What time is it now?' he asked. The Frenchman merely frowned in evident puzzlement. 'The watch you have underneath your stinking, flea-ridden coat. What time does it show?'

Sas's eye twitched. How had the officer known about the watch? He hesitated before opening up his coat to reveal a battered timepiece. He clicked open the lid and showed Hallam its face.

It was five minutes to noon.

Hallam grinned.

The pistol exploded to send the ball straight through the door, to pluck the Frenchman backwards dead onto the ground.

'They're coming!' Hallam slammed the door shut as a volley of musketry struck the doorway.

Benoit screamed and went to get on his feet until Fox stepped forward and smacked him on the head with the butt of his musket. He fell back against the wall, eyes glassy.

'Here they come!' Tipton called, ducking away as glass was shattered by a French bullet.

'Hold your fire!'

'How did you know they were up to something?' Fox asked, then ducked instinctively as a ball smacked through the thatch roof to hit a beam overhead.

'He asked me if I had heard about Jemappes?' Hallam said. 'I lied to him. The colonel likes to discuss battles in the Mess. He thinks it will educate his officers. And those that listen, like me, learn from him. I knew the French had attacked at noon. That's what he was trying to tell his men to do. Benoit has a watch on a chain around his neck. He's been planning for his men to storm the farm.'

Fox looked outraged. 'The conniving bastard.'

'We have to hold this farm,' Hallam said in a low voice, so the sergeant could hear. 'They won't let us live otherwise. So we kill them.'

Fox nodded, gripping the musket tightly so that his knuckles showed white. 'It's them or us, sir.'

Hallam slapped his shoulder. 'Aye, it is. Just make sure it's them.'

'I will, sir.'

Hulse ducked from a shot that thudded into the shutters. Musket smoke was clouding the air outside, and he could only see a couple of shapes. 'I can't see them now, sir!'

Hallam loaded his pistol again, grabbed one of the French muskets and ran to Tipton. He peered outside where a man wearing a green jacket was edging towards the farm, trying to flank them. Hallam brought the musket up and pulled the trigger. The noise was loud. 'If you get a clear view, take a shot!' he yelled to his men. Tipton had emptied the French cartridges into an enemy's upturned bicorn. Hallam plucked one out and began feverishly reloading. Once finished, he ran to Hulse as the door rattled with bullets. Shawford appeared and Hallam ordered him back to the pantry.

'You keep your family safe,' he told him, thrusting the French musket into his hands. 'Your wife knows how to load one. Perhaps she knows how to fire one.' The old soldier understood and disappeared. 'Can you see them now?' he asked Hulse.

A figure moved next to the window and Hallam didn't hesitate. He pointed the pistol at the shape and the ball shot the enemy in the face. There were footsteps and a bayonet lunged through the window towards Hulse. The private saw it coming and twisted away as the blade flashed. Hallam kicked the weapon aside.

'I've got him!' Hulse yelled and his musket banged to shatter the enemy's ribcage.

The door thudded and shook.

'Bastards!' Fox snarled.

Hallam left Hulse loading. He tucked the pistol into his sash and withdrew his sword. It was cumbersome in the tight space, but he would use it to spear the enemy rather than slash. Benoit was still unconscious.

The door shook again and voices cursed. A man laughed evilly. Two bayonets ripped into the wood. Again and again they hacked until a large crack appeared. Boots kicked and Fox, sitting on the chest, moved a fraction. Hallam knew they would enter soon. He rammed his sword into the earthen floor, grabbed hold of Benoit's jacket and tugged it off him. The man stirred and moaned. Hallam kicked him in the face.

'I can't hold them back!' Fox shouted urgently.

Hallam, wearing the jacket over his hands, lifted the bubbling pot off the hook. 'Stand back!'

The door thudded and suddenly swung open as two men tumbled forward. Hallam snarled as he flung the pot's contents at the door where two more men stepped forward. The boiling stew splashed over them, soaking bare flesh and they recoiled as though a cannon had fired grapeshot through the opening. The men shrieked in agony. Fox rammed his bayonet into the nearest prone enemy's neck, twisted it and stepped back. Hallam dropped the empty crock, and whipped his sword free to stab the other Frenchman. A big man, untouched by the redcoats' bullets or stew, charged through the gap, and brushed Fox aside as though he was made of straw. Hallam lunged with his sword, but the blade glanced off the man's musket to entangle itself in his patchwork coat.

Hallam let the sword go and drew the clasp-knife. The Frenchman tried to beat him down with his musket, but Hallam ducked and plunged the knife into his thigh. The big man snorted like a bull, picked him up and tossed him across the room. Hallam smashed into the wall, to collapse on top of Fox who was bleeding from the mouth.

'You ugly bugger!' Shawford exclaimed before shooting the giant with his musket. The Frenchman jerked backwards, but the bullet seemed to have had no effect. He bounded towards Shawford who had gone wide-eyed at the man's doggedness. Behind him Little Jim shrieked.

'No!' Hallam shouted, trying to rise up.

The Frenchman battered Shawford aside. He turned, snarling and Rose shot him with the French musket. The man stumbled with the private clasping his legs. He thumped a massive fist down onto the old soldier's head, but the redcoat hung on. Rose calmly walked up to the giant and put the horse-pistol to his chest and pulled the trigger. Blood sprayed over the wall as the ball tore a length of spine away.

Hallam staggered to the door, clambered over the bodies to see two men running away. Hulse and Tipton fired from the windows and the last man fell dead with a bullet in the back. Hallam let the remaining man go. The wounded French he left, sprawled and screaming from the burns. He didn't care what would happen to them.

'I think we're safe,' he said and sagged back against the wall. He ran a hand across his forehead, smearing grime.

There was a strangulated cry and he rushed back inside thinking there was still was a threat when he found Shawford with his thick calloused hands gripped around Benoit's neck, wringing it like a chicken.

'This one ordered the men to abuse me,' Rose said to Hallam.

Hallam ordered the other redcoats out. Hulse was placed on picquet while Hallam, Fox and Tipton buried Phelps. By the time they had finished, the afternoon light was darkening. Hallam did not ask about Benoit. He had the dead French dragged inside and tossed a burning brand into each of the rooms. It took a while for the flames to spread, but as they walked out of the woods, he heard the roof collapse and turned to watch. It was a place of misery. There was a history of violence there and setting it ablaze felt like it was the right thing to do.

54

A fitting end to such evil men, he considered.

The sky was still smeared with the smoke of the burning as they walked north.

****

It was Christmas Eve.

Icicles hung from branches and redcoats broke through the ice with bayonets to get water from the streams for the cooking pots. Breakfast for some consisted of flour dust, cooked into little dumplings, stale bread, or acorns and old berries found beneath the oaks and bushes. Several officers shot at a plump of ducks passing over, the musket bangs echoed as men looked up in anticipation, but none of the birds fell from the sky and they cursed their poor luck rather than their marksmanship. The vast majority of men had nothing to eat. Bellies were painful and swollen from cramps. Some had to run into the hedgerows to void their bowels. Dysentery and fever were rife.

Grave was a small impoverished town about nine miles southwest of Nijmegan on the left bank of the River Maas. It had been heavily fortified over the centuries, often billeting military troops from Austria, Spain and France, who of late had added embankments, ditches and gun emplacements to the ancient walls that surrounded the town. The large castle was rebuilt and it was here that the Dutch had surrendered to the French just days ago after a brief siege, but it was a poor place filled with memories of destruction, sieges, starvation and misery.

'You see, they can't even bloody well hold onto one of their own towns,' Major Osborne grumpily gave his opinion of the Dutch as he and Colonel Paget espied Grave from a thicket of pine trees less than a mile to the south. He had spent his night in a grotty little farmstead and awoke covered in flea bites. Rain showed above the far hills as a dark stain. 'That's what happens when you arm shit-stinking, clog-wearing peasants with firelocks. They're not an army, they're a goddamn rabble.'

Paget did not reply. He was still smarting at Osborne's impertinence from the bridge. Instead, he looked to where General

55

Sir David Dundas, commander of the British right, and his staff were talking, making notes and giving orders just ahead of the tree line. Paget had grown to dislike Osborne's company and so he clicked his tongue and trotted over towards the group of officers without saying a word to the major.

This wasn't to be Paget's first battle, but he was nevertheless anxious to make a name for himself and not to let the regiment down. It was a fine battalion and men like Captain Richard Hussey Vivian had paid good money to get transferred to the 28th. Vivian had made a name for himself in the last few years and now wanted to transfer to a cavalry regiment, but it was a damned good regiment with a proud history and Paget hoped to continue with its legend.

'Should be a decent day's fighting,' said a voice over to his left.

Paget turned to see an unknown officer trotting along a muddied track; he was also heading towards Dundas.

'So I hear,' Paget replied genially. 'Edward Paget, 28th,' he said, and outstretched his hand when he was close enough.

'Arthur Wesley, 33rd,' said the officer, taking the proffered hand. 'Pleased to make your acquaintance.'

'Likewise,' Paget said. '33rd, eh?' he said, staring at Wesley's red facings. 'I heard about Boxtel.'

Wesley grunted slightly from the mention of the name. The regiment had been part of the British and Hanoverian force that had launched a counter-attack after the French had pushed the Dutch from the town. But the manoeuvre had failed despite the regiment's superb volley fire, which had shattered the French attack.

'I overheard that Sir David reckons the French at Grave will try to keep us pinned back whilst Pichegru marches his army to trap us like fish caught in the nets,' Wesley said. 'There can't be more than a four thousand of the Jacobins here. One whiff of a volley and they'll retreat behind the towns walls and we'll have to endure another siege,' he added bitterly. 'What this army needs to do is consolidate. We're scattered to the winds and all that's left for us to do is drift away like autumn leaves caught in a breeze.'

Wesley was in his twenties, slim, straight-backed and Paget noted he had piercing eyes and a sharp, hooked nose. There was something strange in his manner, impressive in his tone and utterly decisive in his manner.

Paget gave a firm nod of agreement. The trick was to win this small victory, and still bring the British Army to safety in one piece. That would not be easy, and it was all down to other men's decisions.

'We can't endure a winter siege,' he said. 'We have to hope the locals lock the gates behind the French and then they'll be forced to simply surrender.'

Wesley brayed with laughter that caused a few of the older officers around Sir David to scowl at him. He turned to see a sullen company of redcoats march past.

'Driving rain and snow makes men careless, for they are too consumed with their own misery to care,' Wesley commented. 'Or perhaps they are wretched because of their own officers?'

Paget grunted. 'I agree, Wesley. But what to do, eh?'

Wesley pursed his thin lips and stared across at the flat landscape, almost as though he was mesmerised by the bleak beauty of it. 'Have you heard that Robespierre's been toppled?'

'The Directory,' Paget said with disgust. 'One dictator ruling the country is removed so that a whole group of dictators can do the same job. We're fighting a mob, Wesley.'

'Agreed, but the damned mob has beaten us at nearly every turn,' Wesley replied with a wry smile. 'They've seen off the Austrians who have scuttled back across the Rhine and they've taken Antwerp, Brussels, and their armies are chasing us every day away from the sea. We're to help the eastern defences, but we're done here, Paget. We're heavily outnumbered, but still there's nothing right now to cause us undue concern,' he said calmly. 'I heard that the government wants to recall some of our regiments for the Sugar Islands.'

Paget stared. 'Good God,' he uttered, thinking of the West Indies. 'That will leave us with even less manpower.'

'True, Paget, true,' Wesley replied. He brought out an expensive telescope and trained it at the walls where the Tricolour of France flew high from the castle's main tower instead of the Dutch Tricolour. Tall pine trees hid the outlying land and the River Maas.

Then, he traversed it across the fields to the west to a tiny village called Escharen. He watched dark streaks of smoke that betrayed home cooking fires.

'Grave should give the men spirit, Wesley,' Paget considered, 'but I hear that Pichegru is less than two days away. There will be no time to lay a siege, any blockhead can tell you that, so we've got to beat them with volleys and finish them off with the cold steel.'

Wesley smiled, liking Paget's comments. 'The French haven't tasted defeat yet. But we shall see, Paget, we shall see,' he said, smiling and closed his eyepiece. 'I don't know where we're heading, but I do hope our paths will cross again.' He touched his bicorn hat and clicked his heels to spur his horse forward away from the group of officers.

Paget watched him leave and turned to greet a couple of the officers he knew from his Westminster days. It was good to catch up with friends before battle.

****

Julian Stubbington was resigned to death.

He was shivering, sweat-laced and yet his mouth was as dry as saltpetre. He confessed his feelings of his own impending doom to Hallam who told him not to be so damned silly, and to go and get his sword sharpened.

'For whatever use it'll be,' the boy said forlornly, as he disappeared beyond the throng of waking redcoats.

Hallam inspected his own sword to find it dull and blunt. There was a new notch in the tip and he reckoned it was caused by the desperate fight at the farm. Ignoring the pangs of hunger, he too went in search of an armourer. His sword had not been sharpened in days and would not be useful in battle, and this fight today promised to be a big one, unless the French surrendered early. He found a cavalry armourer from the 11th Light Dragoons who gave the sword a razor-like edge. He tossed the man a coin for his trouble and walked back to the battalion just as dawn was breaking.

Hallam stared across a flooded field that was pitted with soft rain, where a short-eared owl glided silently in the gloom. Just above the horizon the first arc of sunlight flared orange despite the swollen clouds. He stared at the glorious bright light that seemed to pulse and flirted with the idea that it might be a sunny day, and then dismissed it as whimsy.

Smoke from the camp fires seemed to stretch up to the star-flecked sky. There were a lot of men around each fire where the wood crackled and spat and popped in the rain. Their faces were gaunt, drained and unshaven, but they were glad of the warmth. One man with brown teeth laughed at a poor joke, and another poked inside a bandage tied around his head where a sword cut from a hussar had taken an eye. Hallam saw him wipe his wet finger on his jacket.

'Tea, sir?' Private Tipton asked him.

'Have you got any?' Hallam said dubiously.

'I managed to trade a silver knife for some tea leaves and a new pipe from one of the lads in the 33rd this morning, sir,' Tipton said as he poured some tea into a mug. 'It came with an ounce of tobacco as well,' he added happily.

'It's a good trade,' Hallam replied. He sipped the hot liquid, savouring the taste and letting its warmth seep down deep into his cold body. 'That's damned good,' he said appreciatively and Tipton grinned. 'Where did you get the knife?'

Tipton shuffled his feet and cuffed snot from his pointy nose. 'Found it, sir.'

'On its own, or was it with a set?' Hallam said wryly, knowing that Tipton had stolen it.

'Wish I had tea back last week, sir,' Tipton said, changing the subject. 'When I was on picquet duty with Appleton. We could have done with a mug of it then. Poor bloody Appleton. It's not right for a soldier to go like that.' He shook his head in sadness at the memory of his companion who had frozen to death during the night.

Since the farm, the private looked older. They must all have aged in the campaign. *Cold, hunger and fear does that to a man*, Hallam reflected.

'Let's hope we lose no more of our boys to the damned cold.'

'Amen to that, sir,' Tipton said. 'I should have known something was wrong as he was a talker. There were times you couldn't shut him up.'

'I seem to remember him being punished for talking on parade?'

Tipton chuckled. 'That was him, sir. Talked right under the ears of Major Osborne. The clumsy oaf.' The private looked awkward for a moment. 'I meant Appleton being the clumsy one, sir, not the good major.' A thin strand of greasy hair slipped out from underneath his hat that he tucked back with rag-wrapped fingers.

The men should have had their hair powdered white into a pigtail called a queue, which originally was to prevent long hair from impeding a soldier's vision. Each man's hair was hauled back, greased with candle wax, and then twisted about a small sand-filled leather bag that was secured with a strip of leather so that the hair hung stiff at the nape. The white hair looked neat and tidy on the parade ground, but was a haven for lice and caused misery. Like most things, it had been abandoned during the campaign.

Hallam wondered whether Tipton was being facetious on purpose, admitting that he thought Osborne incompetent and yet unable to voice that opinion. Hallam declined to comment. He stared at the glowing cinders and his thoughts turned to Isabel, remembering that she preferred lemon in her tea and how he had wrinkled his face at the taste and how she had laughed at him. Her sweet laugh echoed in his mind and he smiled. He wondered what she would be doing now on Christmas Eve. She had a large happy family and no doubt plucked pheasant, partridge and other wildfowl along with smoked hams would be hanging from the kitchen walls and Hallam's favourite: a haunch of mutton would be ready for the spit. More food such as brawn, potted venison, roast goose, stuffing, applesauce and well-buttered mashed potatoes would complement the main course. Dessert would be rich plum pudding, fruit cake, eggnog, spruce beer and the hot, fruity and spicy wassail drink. Christmas was a time to be at home, warming next a hearth-fire, surrounded by loved ones and thinking nothing of peace, drink and good food. Instead, this morning they would do battle and some men would never see another Christmas.

Hallam blinked out of his glorious dream. 'You didn't acquire any food by any chance?'

''Fraid not, sir.'

Hallam smiled. 'What happened to that ham at the farmhouse?'

'I'm not sure what you mean, sir.'

'No, nobody does,' Hallam said sarcastically. 'I definitely saw one hanging from the beams.'

Tipton sniffed. 'Perhaps it went up in smoke like the Frenchies, sir?'

'Ah well, it was probably not pork.'

The private stared and wiped his nose again. 'What do you think it was, sir?'

'Probably not worth imagining,' Hallam said, with a lop-sided grin. 'Being that it had been in French hands for weeks, it could have been anything. Goat, horse, deer. Or worse. Far worse. It's not unheard of that men when they cannot get food turn on themselves to feed their empty bellies.' He let the thought sink in. 'Still as you said all up in smoke. Ah well. Probably for the best. Make sure you give Mister Stubbington a cup of your tea.'

'I will, sir,' Tipton said, face suddenly ashen.

'Are you all right?'

Tipton's jaw lolled, eyes widening and Adam's apple bobbing in a pronounced gulp. 'I don't feel well, sir. I've had too much...tea.' With that the private shot from the fire to head towards the latrines.

Hallam broke into laughter. He stayed longer than he wished because the fire was so inviting, thinking the moment that he moved away, the chill would return to haunt him like the freezing grasp of a spirit. He drained the cup and returned to find Stubbington who was still morose and subdued. It wasn't like him. He was always cheerful and Hallam realised that the imminent battle was infecting him with fear. He understood the familiar gut-wrenching, bowel-loosening feeling.

'I was like you on the morning of my very first battle,' Hallam tried to soothe him as the first battalions were being ordered to form up in the battle lines. The rain had ceased and a harrying wind blew raw.

'I'm not scared, sir,' Stubbington replied tartly as though Hallam had questioned his nerve. He flicked a piece of dirt from a faded yellow sleeve and ignored the writhing in his guts.

The redcoats looked like tramps. A private who had lost his hat had a strip of dirty cloth wrapped around his head to protect his ears. One or two privates had French, Austrian and Dutch infantry packs and one even wore outlandish Hungarian breeches. Hallam looked at his own uniform; one of his knees was visible and his frayed greatcoat was speckled with blood and grime.

Hallam watched three émigré contingents march past, their moustached faces showed that they were eager to prove their worth in the imminent battle; nevertheless, he watched them with suspicious eyes. He'd seen a few foreign units collapse in disorder on the march and even one who, frightened by their own volley, had fled the field.

The first was Loewenstein's Chasseurs, a rifle armed German regiment clad in a uniform of blue-grey with green facings and black round hats topped with dark green plumes that matched the tall thick forests of their country. They were preceded by more Germans from Hompesch's Chasseurs, a unit that had been mauled at Boxtel and suffered in the retreat so much that only a hundred men were fit for today's battle. They carried carbines and long rifles and were clothed in dark green coats faced red. The last contingent was a mixture of cavalry and infantry who wore sky blue coats with black facings. The Damas regiments, consisting mostly of French émigrés, were raised for Dutch service, and had fought in this campaign as hard as any British redcoat regiment.

As the foreign troops marched onto the field, the 28th was ordered to form up alongside the 27th and Loewenstein's Germans on the British right flank from line into column. The 80th; volunteers from Staffordshire, Hompesch's greencoats and the Loyal Emigrants; a red-coated regiment who had already gained an excellent fighting reputation, formed the centre while the 19th and 33rd; men from the Yorkshire dales, formed the left flank. The 42nd, tough Scotsmen from the mountains and wild glens, the infantry companies from the Damas Legion and a thinned regiment of yet more French ex-Royalists called Autichamp, were held in reserve. Damas' Hussars,

62

Rohan's 1st Hussars, the 11th and 15th Light Dragoons covered the flanks whilst two foot artillery batteries were dragged behind the reserve, giving the allied force a total of nine thousand men.

'The first thing to do is to stay calm,' Hallam said. 'The men look to their mates, but they look to their officers first. You might not see them, but they'll be looking for steely courage. As officers, we cannot show fear.'

'I said I'm not scared, sir.' Stubbington felt his skin prickle with sweat.

Hallam was watching the regiment's form up. 'More often than not, they'll be just lines of men facing each other. Both similar numbers and both armed with muskets. You'll find no one has an edge. At least that's what they think. But we do.'

'Sir?'

'We get in close and at fifty yards our volley fire will destroy them. You'll be amazed at how easy it is to miss, but at fifty yards or less our practised musketry will punish them.'

'Because we load faster, sir?'

'Exactly.'

A thudding of hooves made Hallam turn to see a slim staff officer galloping along the fields. The man curbed his mount as he neared Paget and Osborne. Hallam tried to read their lips, but the range was too far. After a brief moment, the officer saluted and spurred his horse towards the 27th.

Hallam turned back to Stubbington. 'Do you know something? I'm scared,' he confessed, before flicking his eyes back at the staff officer. He was deeply nervous because he kept thinking about Isabel, a fear that seared through his veins. He missed her and kept thinking that it would be cruel if he was killed when he had only just found true love and married. He had no intention of attending that Ball in Lyndhurst, but somehow he had gone and it was then that cupid's arrow had struck with the accuracy of a German rifle. It wouldn't be fair, to die so far from home, from Isabel, but he also knew it was a soldier's life that he had chosen and knew what fate might have for him.

'You're scared, sir?' Stubbington knew Hallam was trying to soothe him, but he could not get the vision of death from his mind.

His stomach clenched like a fist. Last night he dreamt that he had died in the battle. He saw whole files of men blown to scraps before his eyes and then he was hit and he felt nothing. He saw his blue feather drift away. And that was it; he was dead, gone into oblivion.

'Of course,' Hallam said, 'and doubtless some will say it gets easier, but they've probably never fought a proper battle before, or they are bluffing to cover their own nerves. I've seen men, with years of campaigning trod under their boots, stricken with fear. It makes men cry, vomit or petrified to the spot.'

'An officer should set an example, sir,' Stubbington said, gnawing his upper lip.

'They should.'

'So I've taken courage in the form of brandy. A sip or two, but I will remain at my post. I will not let the Slashers down. I will not let you down, sir.' He wore his issued greatcoat, which bulked up his frame and the sword at his hip showed that he was a warrior. However, the ensign knew he did not cut an imposing figure, for his shoulders were too narrow, his skin was soft like a girl's and he could not yet grow facial hair.

'I never suspected for one second that you would, Mister Stubbington,' Hallam replied as he negotiated a large ice-rimmed puddle. 'I joined up as a youngster like you.'

'Why did you enlist?'

Hallam did not answer straight away. He looked to the company. Morale was certainly low, but as they marched in silence, Hallam detected the old feeling of pride from them; a pride that would carry them through to the very end like it had always done so.

'I wanted to live a boy's adventure tale,' Hallam said. 'I wanted to lead men into battle. I wanted to know what pride, honour and sacrifice meant. I wanted to feel alive.'

'And have you accomplished that, sir?'

Hallam grinned. 'Oh yes.'

The army had brought him opportunities: promotion, enrichment, education and escape from a life of possible drudgery and toil. It had given him everything he had wanted.

Hallam stared up at the town's stone walls that were high and imposing. In front of them, the land was darkening and he realised the French demi-brigades were similarly advancing. He wondered if a seasoned officer was giving advice to a junior in the enemy ranks.

'We all get premonitions and omens,' Hallam continued, 'it's natural before a fight. Try to remain calm, stay at your post and you'll do all right.'

'I suppose so, sir,' Stubbington said gloomily.

'Have you had your sword cleaned and honed?'

A troubled expression clouded Stubbington's usually happy countenance. 'I forgot, sir. I was waylaid by the hope of brandy. I apologise.'

Hallam shot him a grin. 'As an ensign, I couldn't walk into battle without running a whetstone across the blade every morning. I considered it bad luck. Just pray that if you have to use it, that it will do its job. And the first thing you do after the fight is...?'

'Get it sharpened, sir,' Stubbington grinned.

Hallam's stomach rumbled painfully. It already felt like a tight knot, but he was desperately hungry and had to force a hand across his belly to try to soothe it. His breakfast consisted of a lump cut from a flitch of bacon fat and a piece of hard dark bread coated in rancid butter. Grave was crammed full of wine, food and women so it was rumoured, which meant of course that it wasn't, but the lie was said to encourage the British. The cellars, it was said, were packed with casks, bottles and wineskins, the storehouses jammed full with boxes, sacks and barrels of food and the women, all beautiful and long-legged, were starved of sex.

'Now if you're still nervous when you see the bastards, just think about all the young girls waiting for you inside,' Hallam said. 'They're on their backs right now waiting for you to give them your British beef.'

The young officer laughed as he was supposed to, and then clasped his ears from the thunderous roar that came from outside of the town.

The French artillery had opened fire.

It was six o'clock.

****

65

Every gun outside the walls opened fire.

The salvo showed as an eruption of flame-speared smoke as if a giant fantastical beast had awoken from a deep slumber, roaring, angry and terrifying. The smoke pumped yellow-grey that mingled with the mist so that the gun batteries were instantly obscured.

A heartbeat or so later, the sound of the cannon was ear-shattering and slammed across the frosted fields like a giant's whip-crack. The sound was enough to fill the hearts of their enemies with dread and told them that the soldiers of the French Revolutionary army were no pushovers.

The battle for Grave promised to be a bloody one.

The majority of the guns were loaded with roundshot. The cold barrels dropped the heavy iron balls short of the advancing redcoats that skittered and skipped harmlessly along the ploughed fields. The howitzers were armed with shell and the burning fuses were extinguished in the puddles, dykes and snow drifts. Hallam watched one roundshot slash through the branches of a willow tree to bounce and smash apart a fence post and come to a thudding halt against the ruins of an old farm building.

Stubbington had never seen so many guns. He knew the French always brought more cannon, more so than the allies combined, and yet somehow nothing had prepared him for actually seeing the great banks of gun smoke where the host waited.

General Sir William Harcourt's ADC came to summon the brigade forward. Another rider galloped past the 28th, sending clods of earth up into the air. A small clump hit Stubbington below the ear. He wiped the mud away, but it left a dirty mark.

'Forward march,' Paget called. 'At the double.'

Captain Ingram's Light Company was at the head of the column, jogging across the snowy fields, packs and equipment bouncing as they went. They were already exhausted and the men panted and gulped for breath.

The glowing slow-matches of the portfires touched the quills and the French twelve pounders crashed back on their long trails. The guns sent their missiles straight across the fields, the balls smashing and bouncing their way towards the redcoats. Every time a roundshot hit the ground, it churned snow and dirt as it bounced away in a blur. A cannonball missed Paget's horse by a hair's breadth.

Each column was separated by enough distance so that they could form into line if necessary. The redcoats ran on and then suddenly the damp air was punctuated with the screams of the first dying men as enemy gunfire found targets. A single shot bounced down the rank and took the heads off of half a dozen men from Ingram's company. Battalion men coming up behind dodged the corpses and wet patches of glistening gore.

'Keep your dressing!' Sergeant Fox, sporting a bruised jaw from the attack at the farm, bellowed at a man who had bent down to loot a dead Light Bob. Corporal Beckett instantly grabbed the man and shoved him back into his file.

Roundshot flicked one private aside like a child's toy, and then skidded low to take the legs off of two men standing beside Hallam.

'Forward!' Clements shouted angrily, his head aching from the schnapps he had stolen from the house that the quartermaster had commandeered in the night. It was a small farm, but the man had a large cellar and the regiments' officers had all helped themselves to dozens of bottles and jars. His stomach felt like it was on fire and his bowels loose with water, but he stayed in the saddle and hoped it would pass. It usually did, and after the battle, he would finish off the last two bottles and everything would be all right until he could acquire some more.

The gunners swabbed and rammed after each shot, but the officers saw that although the missiles had slashed into the red ranks, the gaps had instantly closed and the ranks were still advancing, almost as though the missiles had caused no casualties. Drummers beat frantically and the Frenchmen cheered. Men were singing *la Marseillaise*, the Revolutionary anthem. Quills were put back into the vents, the gunners ducked aside, and the guns roared to life again.

'Form line here!' The ADC raised his arm to indicate the spot.

The 28th wheeled into line. The sergeants kept the men moving and then jostled and shouted at them to redress the ranks. The bandsmen at the rear beat the drums in rhythm to the manoeuvre.

Roundshot could disembowel, decapitate or take a limb off, but a shell, landing in the packed ranks could devastate. Hallam watched Tipton stop a shell with a boot and knock the fizzing fuse clean from the charge with a hard smack of his musket butt. Tipton was the joker of the company, likeable, sometimes disobedient and a prankster, but his quick-witted action had just saved lives.

'Well done, boy!' Fox said approvingly and Tipton grinned.

The guns hammered and the ground shook. This was the French way of war, deluging the line with artillery bombardments, pounding and pulverising the enemy infantry. Hallam doubted that any of his men had ever seen or heard so many French guns blasting their iron throats free. Every now and again, there was a pause in the thunderous cannonade, and it seemed so unreal that Hallam wondered whether his ears were too beaten to hear anything until he caught the saint sound of drums, cheering and the thud of marching men.

The smoke from the French guns rolled across the fields and the air began to darken and choke. The cannon fire was sporadic as the gun teams that reloaded the quickest were firing more often. Hallam watched the guns, the jets of smoke and the flame-points entranced him. But as they got closer, the shots screamed as the balls arced higher from warm barrels.

'Onward, you humbugs!' Osborne croaked, sword tip tracing manic circles above his head. 'Onward!'

Hallam could see people watching the ensuing battle from the houses and walls and one or two daring ones on rooftops. He could not see any Dutch flags and wondered if the townsfolk were on the side of the French and would help repel the British assault.

A shell plunged deep into one of the dykes and Hallam heard the fuse fizzle loudly as the iron-grey water doused the charge. Another landed in a snow bank and Hallam was surprised when it exploded. Fortuitously, the snow soaked up the blast, a piece of red-hot casing, trailing smoke, smacked harmlessly against his ankle.

A flock of jackdaws speared the air like a sudden torrent of arrows slashing down from loosed war bows to the British right. They shrieked and made their distinct raw sounding call. To some, it sounded mocking. Rooks and crows followed in loose formation, flapping and raining down amongst the oak and elm trees as though they were launching their own assault.

'Bastard birds are laughing at us!' Tipton said.

'A collection of crows is called a murder...' Hulse began, then faltered. Tipton gave him a withering look.

Bugles sounded and hundreds of French skirmishers ran out to meet the attacking red lines. Whistles blew shrill and the British Light Companies and those from the émigré battalions ran out to meet their French equivalents. At first, they came in a loose mass of men; running and firing, and some used the cover of the few trees, fences, snow banks, but most aimed and fired with their firing partners, and then ran on again spreading themselves into a chain.

Some of the German troops were armed with long-barrelled *jäger* hunting rifles and Hallam saw one shoot a French officer clean off his horse. One of the French émigré skirmishers was wounded and Hallam saw his hands go up in surrender, but was viciously bayoneted by his assailant. The Revolutionaries never took émigrés' prisoner, because they were everything that stood against their new found ideals. They despised them.

'*Allez!*' a French officer shouted and the skirmishers sprinted forward to shorten the range and overwhelm the émigré Chasseurs with their slow loading rifles.

A German fired, and immediately ran back to where his firing partner was crouched, waiting and watching for enemies while he reloaded.

'Watch him!' a British officer warned, as a bullet tore up the snow beneath him. 'He's a cocky bastard and I want him dead!'

A group of six Frenchmen dashed forward, but they were seen by other German's and redcoats and the musket and rifle fire threw all the Frenchmen down to leave one crawling and another rolling over in agony.

Hallam was watching a French officer with a tanned face with long flowing blond hair. He was waving his men on with a grim determination. Hallam thought him confident and probably a hero to his men. Bullets plucked the air about him, but he still gave his men inspiring orders to achieve glory. His sword blade flickered with sunlight and then suddenly there was a broad red stain spreading across his chest and his arms went high and wide, head flopped back, as the man toppled to the ground. Dead. A hero dead, just like that.

Four squadrons of French Hussars suddenly appeared on a sunken road over on the British right and the Light troops were immediately called back. British Light Dragoons spurred towards them, bugles sounding, and the French skirmishers returned to their units. The redcoats jeered them loudly, even though the allies had just retreated.

'Don't you know what day it is?' Lieutenant Colonel Paget asked no one in particular as he trotted his horse forward, swerving past a spent roundshot. He looked energetic and cheerful. 'It's Christmas Eve! Time to rejoice!'

'I'll celebrate when we leave this damned country, sir,' Hallam replied dryly.

The Slashers, the Inniskillings and the German riflemen advanced steadily until the ground dipped to where two French battalions were rushing towards them. A hedgerow, whitened and crusted with ice, acted as a natural screen between the two opposing sides: on the right, near the road, a collapsed house offered limited protection. A blackbird flew from the branches over to the exposed rafters of the ruin.

'Ensign Bennett!' Major Osborne shouted at the young officer at the front of the battalion whose job was to carry the Regimental Colour, the silk flag bearing the regiment's facings. In the centre of the yellow field was a padded red shield with 'twenty-eight' in golden Roman numerals and 'REG', surrounded by a Union wreath. 'Hold that bloody Colour high, man! I want the damned Frenchie-bastards to see who they face!' A second ensign carried the Kings' Colour, which was the flag of Great Britain.

Hallam saw both flags rise higher, both flapping in the buffeting wind. He felt proud of the regiment and his spine always tingled at the sight of the unfurled 28th's Colours.

A howitzer shell exploded some distance to the regiment's front; hot wind fanned Hallam's face and scraps of casing and other debris churned the ground.

The French infantry marched head-on with their muskets resting on their shoulders, as if they would just simply brush the impudent enemy aside. Mouths opened wide as the men chanted the anthem.

70

'Keep your dressing!' Fox's voice carried with ease and brooked no argument. 'Dress the ranks, you dirty bastards!'

'That's the way! Steady!' Paget was calm and his unruffled composure instilled confidence in the battalion. 'Forward, my brave Slashers!'

'Are you still with us, Mister Stubbington?' Hallam asked without turning his head.

'Yes, sir!'

'Good man.'

A shell exploded in between the two British regiment's and a handful of men in the rear file were tossed into the air like rag dolls. One had the side of his head shorn away, and another had his spine laid open. One of the men was screaming because an arm and a leg were nothing but bloodied stumps. Another shell fired too high exploded harmlessly in mid-air.

The gap closed to a hundred yards between the opposing forces and the British, faces red with exertion and hearts pounding, were still advancing and the French halted. They formed up behind the frozen hedgerow in line. Muskets poked through branches. Officers pushed more men into positions. Hallam counted the barrels, estimating there appeared to be about a thousand of the enemy, the same number as the three allied regiments combined.

The drums and chanting rose to a crescendo behind them. Hallam could see the moustached and bearded faces clearly now. Unknown faces stared back in hatred, terror, or the familiar look of utter coolness. The French were experienced soldiers and their victories had given them an edge as sharp as a well-honed sabre. One officer was on horseback and kept galloping up and down the French lines. He raised and pointed his sabre at the British, his long cloak flapped in the wind.

'Where's our bleeding cavalry gone?' Tipton asked.

The drums beat louder now because the enemy guns had stopped firing for fear of hitting their own men. Voices seemed to echo.

'Keep your mouth shut, Private!' Fox shouted.

At sixty yards Hallam heard the French officer shout, '*tirez!*' and then instantly the whole line fogged dirty white; a split second later, Hallam heard the explosion of musketry.

Tipton's head was jerked back as a neat hole was punched in his forehead. The ball erupted from the back of his skull to spray the man in the rear file behind him with his blood and brains. Ensign Bennett holding the Regimental Colours collapsed with a bullet in his lung. A private wearing clogs, stuffed with straw, hobbled for a moment after a ball slashed his calf, then after discovering it was just a flesh wound resumed his pace. Perhaps twenty men were felled by the massive volley. The French had expected to kill and wound many more, but Hallam simply put it down to the range, or damp, or poor saltpetre in the powder.

He saw Frenchmen trying to break down a section of the hedgerow, and heard enemy cheers and shouted orders from the gun smoke blanketing their front. More shadowed figures behind them made the enemy line more impressive and yet more terrifying.

A lone shell screamed overhead to explode behind Hallam's company. Debris showered the men and something wet struck his neck. He wiped it away, eyes still focussed on the enemy.

'Close up to the front!' Paget shouted.

The NCOs repeated the instruction all along the line. When men fell, the normal practice was to pull the wounded or dead behind the line and then edge towards the centre to fill the gap. If losses were heavy, this would keep the line three deep, but made the frontage even narrower. Paget wanted the front rank full at all times, so if a front rank man fell, the man directly behind was to step into his file.

Hallam saw Fox haul Tipton's body to the rear. The old sergeant laid him out gently, a look of sorrow on his battered face. Fox had been harsh on the younger men, in order to mould them into steady soldiers, but the boy's death had genuinely affected him.

'Halt! Make ready!' Paget ordered. The French saw the British line ripple, as though the men had turned to the right.

'Let's send the bastards our goodwill!' Hallam shouted over the sound of five hundred muskets being cocked.

Then something caught his eye; it whirled about his boots, dancing and skipping in the small wind. He bent down to pick it up. Strange, it was a blue feather. What the hell was it doing out here?

''Talion! Present!' Paget ordered. 'Fire!'

A thunderous explosion jetted out that flickered and stabbed bright flames. The air was instantly engulfed in the wretched smell of rotten eggs and with a tangle of death. The disciplined fusillade ripped into the French, breaking through the hedges to twitch and turn the front ranks to red ruin.

'Load!' Paget steadied his horse. 'I declare them out!' he shouted half-laughing, as if commenting on a cricket match.

Hallam was still staring at the feather when he realised what it meant. His fingers turned it over leaving it blood-smeared. He twisted around to where Stubbington should be, but the junior officer was missing. Hallam cast an eye on the red rags that dotted in the snow behind as the regiment had advanced. A man wailed loudly for his mother and the less badly hurt yelled for help or for their friends to come and fetch them.

'Mister Stubbington?' Hallam called, looking around as the ensign was never at his post preferring to be close to his side.

'To your place, Lieutenant!' Clements said.

Hallam caught sight of Corporal Beckett who had just run back from collecting ammunition and spare flints from the bodies and his eyes told him everything he needed to know.

Stubbington was dead; blown to pieces by the last shell in an instant. Hallam touched the back of his neck again and withdrew his fingers. They were sticky and glistened red.

'I said, to your place!' Clements shouted at him.

Hallam could not speak, he was in shock. The boy had known he would die and stood at his post. Hallam was suddenly hit with remorse and guilt for the ensign who had only wanted to learn. He had become impatient with the sixteen-year-old, often rebuking his remarks. He rubbed away the prick of tears, unaware his rough fingers left traces of blood behind.

'Stubbington's dead, sir,' he mumbled.

'Another loss with no one to mourn,' the captain said heartlessly. He drew his pistol, cocked it and aimed it at the French. 'Useless little blighter. His mother should have kept her knees together.' The flint snapped forward and smoke blotted his view.

Hallam shook his head to clear his thoughts; the grieving would have to wait until later. He could hear the ramrods scrape in barrels, could see their looks of alarm on the French faces as the allies brought their muskets to shoulders. There was a battle to win.

Another company of the green-coated riflemen were running up to extend the line. Their captain gave Hallam a smile as he passed. 'Send them to hell, *ja!*'

The French managed another volley; it was weak and ragged because some men were looting bodies, or trying to back away, but one or two shots found targets. A private of the 27th was hit in the neck and he continued the motions of loading until he collapsed from the loss of blood. A sergeant from the 28th, armed with a halberd, was shot through the eye and the weapon spun away from his sprawling form.

'Aim low! Aim low!' Paget's voice was snatched by the wind. 'Fire!'

The redcoats fired another murderous volley and the musket balls buzzed, whistled and slashed into the French ranks. The officer on horseback was struck by a bullet that tore through an elbow, his curved sword dangled useless from its wrist strap. He bent over and turned his mount away.

Volley after volley turned the air thick with acrid smoke. The muskets slammed back into bruised shoulders and hands reached for the next cartridge. The ranks levelled their firelocks and fired when ordered too. They could not aim. The enemy was hidden by the banks of jaundiced white smoke, so it was simply a question of pointing the muzzle and pulling the trigger.

Hallam saw some of his men were hit. Corporal Beckett was shot through both thighs as he stood pulling cartridges free from a wounded man. He staggered, then collapsed and was unceremoniously dragged away by Fox. Private Shawford lost part of his ear to a French ball. He hissed but continued loading and firing with blood dripping down his neck.

'We're hurting them! 28th!' Paget shouted, his voice betraying happiness brought by their success. 'Fix bayonets!'

'Now for some killing, boys,' Fox said darkly, over the sound of the blades being slotted. 'Butcher them like hogs.'

A few shapes loomed in the smoke in front of Hallam. He brought his sword up as a French officer lunged. Sparks slid down the blades as Hallam parried. A second figure appeared with a musket-tipped bayonet. Fox shot the man in the face and he was pitched back in a spray of blood.

'Kill the Frenchie bastard, sir!' a voice called behind Hallam.

The enemy officer was tall, lithe and strong and Hallam felt the blows were already weakening his sword-arm. The man withdrew his arm, then flicked it back to slice open Hallam's forearm. The blade flashed away. Hallam growled, lunged and kicked the man in the knee as he stepped forward. The Frenchman slashed the air in front of him to dispel any attack as he reeled. Hallam knocked the sword away, reached out and grabbed him by the collar. He punched the man in the face with the sword's guard, then bringing his sword up, tugged the enemy onto the well-honed blade. The steel sliced up through the Frenchman's belly, spurting blood as though it were a full wineskin. The officer let out a high-pitched yell as Hallam twisted the sword free and then chopped down through his throat to splatter the ground crimson.

'That's the way to do it, sir,' said the same voice.

The Germans, having loaded their rifles, fired a ragged exchange and more French tumbled to the floor. One man screamed so loud that it was all anyone could hear for an instance. A lieutenant was hit by a musket ball that shattered a rib, and stumbled to the rear with his arm around the shoulders of one of his men, who had taken a ball to the arm. Then, the Germans promptly slotted brass-hilted sword-bayonets before the regiment moved forward.

Paget trotted to the front. 'Advance!' he shouted, waving his sword. 'For England and King George!'

The allied battalions marched and the French infantry retreated, but men who controlled the urge to flee or those who were more disciplined covered their ground with another volley that shook the allied lines.

Hallam heard the sound of the balls hitting flesh and rapping on equipment. He felt a sudden blow to his chest and he staggered for a moment from the impact. He looked down at his coat fearing he'd been shot and saw a smouldering hole. An image of Isabel flashed in his mind. Widowed at such a young age. But he felt no pain and undid the buttons. The bullet had passed through his jacket to strike his timepiece. The watch had shattered and was destroyed, but it had saved his life. He breathed a sigh of heartfelt relief.

'Not your time, sir,' Shawford said.

Hallam grinned. 'Very droll,' he said. 'Allow me to offer the same regard to you too.'

Breath plumed in the air like the billowing of cannon smoke as men grunted with exertion, pain, or fear.

'Close up!' The sergeants shouted the litany of battle. 'Close up!'

'Forward!' Paget said. 'Push them back, you rogues!' A ball snatched at his cocked hat. He had his sword drawn. The drummers were beating a frantic rhythm behind the regiment. 'By fire and by steel! We'll give the French a damned good thrashing!'

The French infantry scrambled away and the artillery, who had been waiting patiently, wanted to cause more casualties so resumed firing.

Roundshot scarred the plain, flinging up soil and stones and bloody fragments of the men caught in their path. Something thudded into Hallam's shoulder and then fell to the ground. He looked down to see that it was a piece of jaw, complete with ragged flesh still attached to the bone.

A bullet hit a private, who was wearing a horse blanket over his coat, square in the chest and he fell backwards to entangle himself with the man in the rear rank. Fox saw this and went to pull the two men apart, when a roundshot fired from a gun that had been angled to inflict as many injuries as possible, slammed into the group of men, tearing Fox's left leg off at the thigh. The sergeant, covered in entrails and blood, twitched as blood pumped bright red on the snow.

'That's the way! Push them! Don't let them stand!' Paget continued his hoarse encouragements. His sword reflected the reddening sun as it slipped towards the horizon.

The British artillery began firing and the first shells exploded in the French ranks outside the town's walls. A riderless horse galloped across the fields, another lay kicking and bleeding.

The same private who had stopped to loot a corpse did it again. This time Hallam saw him, kicked him, punched the back of his head, and led him back into his file.

76

The men from Staffordshire suffered at the hands of a forward battery of guns that fired canister; a whole file was mowed down as the tin cans exploded from the cannon's mouths and the bullets shredded the men like a giant blunderbuss. A Grenadier hit by a ball, spun, fell, then dripped blood as he struggled to his hands and knees. Another doubled up as a ball shattered his hip, but his sharp cries were lost as the battalion cheered. Yet, the regiment advanced unperturbed and the French commander ordered the guns brought back rather than leave them to be captured.

The soldiers of the new revolution were also dying. The steady redcoat and allied battalions were leaving pockets of bodies behind, but their volleys were faster and so the Frenchmen died from lethal musket and rifle fire.

Paget's horse stepped carefully over the bodies, which were once red, but were now in a myriad of colours, the grim water-mark of battle.

There was a loud British cheer from his left. Then, the centre brigade fired a volley before going forward, bayonets extended.

'28th! Charge!' Paget yelled as loudly as he could, putting spurs to his horse as men ran past either side of him.

A light infantryman stumbled, blood spreading fast where his white cross-belts met in the centre of his jacket. Hallam felt a ball flick his sleeve as he ran. His boots squelched in guts strung blue from a disembowelled enemy. He jumped a dying German who was sprawled in that ungainly way that only those deep in sleep could ever match. A French skirmisher with ragged hole in his neck, lay on his back, staring up at the iron-grey sky. Hallam noticed that the man's eyes were wet with tears.

'Charge!' Hallam shouted, as he ran, sword reddened with blood, thrusting it toward the mass of enemy. Muskets fired. One ball plucked at the hem of his coat, tearing a piece of it away. A ramrod cartwheeled overhead, making a strange thrumming sound. 'Come on!' A redcoat lay on his belly; blood had erupted from his mouth to stain a foot of melting snow.

The clash between the Light Dragoons and Hussars continued until the French demi-brigades shattered like a glass goblet and retreated back inside the town. Even an extra squadron of Hussars did not help the matter for they milled about in confusion as the fighting French horse thundered back past them, showering the ground with clods of rigid earth. The cavalry retreated behind the walls covered by blasts of canister that emptied half a dozen British saddles before bugles frantically called them back to safety.

'Packs!' Men were shouting. Some of the French desperate to get away had dropped their muskets and packs to go faster. 'Food! Food!'

Then, a white flag hung from the dilapidated town walls and miraculously, incongruously, astonishingly, the battle was over.

****

The French barred the gates. This allowed them to retreat unmolested west along the winding Maas. They had not wanted to surrender, but the townsfolk were unhappy about a siege and they could not take another blockade. The town had almost been destroyed by siege work some years ago and they had worked hard to rebuild it, so the French had slipped away without spilling further bloodshed. The British were surprised at that, but its battalions were in no state to follow them.

A portly mayor with an orange moustache and side-whiskers welcomed the generals and the British were cheered by the deprived Dutch townsfolk who lined the streets with meagre offerings of oysters, smoked sausages, cabbages, cheese, beer, mussels and smoked eels. There was little bread. It had been a ruinous harvest before the snow came. It had rained for weeks and the rye crops had just rotted in the fields. What little bread available was poor quality, or charged at nearly six times the price.

But as the survivors thanked them, bought food and loaded the wounded onto carts, cavalry scouts detected a huge dark smear on the horizon.

The enemy vanguard.

The British understood that the retreating French had simply joined the larger force and their army was less than five miles away. They would be here within the hour. General Harcourt made an agonising decision to abandon the town and withdrawal north-east fast across the waters of the Maas to the allied held town of Nijmegen.

Seeing and smelling the food, and then being ordered to march away, was enough to make the hungry sob. Some redcoats were so distressed that they broke ranks to drown their sorrows in the wine shops and cellars. Those men not able to be controlled looted and plundered and were made insensible from the alcohol that they drank to forget their grief. They were abandoned to the enemy like the wounded that could not be taken wept and called out for friends, or loved ones. Even those too exhausted to continue lay down with the dead.

The cannon-fire had left the landscape scarred and corpse strewn. The dead were left unburied and the British, phantoms covered in rags, continued their retreat.

By the early afternoon, thirty thousand French soldiers crossed the wide River Waal and marched along the banks to Grave where the vanguard pursued the British along the northern road. The allied defences were gone and so was its thinning army.

****

The tired, despondent and bloodied army followed the road north, which was heavily potholed with a myriad of ruts and cracks. Mud sucked at boots and hooves, and the wheels of the remaining wagons and guns, got stuck in the glutinous slime and had to be pulled free. Those that couldn't be dragged with ease were simply abandoned. Equipment became heavy on tired, aching bodies and packs and haversacks were discarded. The road was a deep ugly scar across the hoary wilderness.

Hallam thought of Isabel: timid, intelligent and yet so elegantly beautiful. In a field of snow and mud and under a grey sky, the image of her seemed to shine like a beacon. From the first moment of their introduction, his devotion to her was unflinching. He longed to see her again. Soon, he hoped, soon.

It was nearly midnight when the regiment limped into the town and as the men collapsed from exhaustion, the officers immediately hunted inns, wine stores and warm billets.

'This place stinks like a whore's crotch,' Hulse complained.

'It's the best we have at the moment so be thankful for it,' Hallam gave the reproach. 'I'd rather have a whore's crotch on my face, stinking or not, than another night out open under the stars. At least it'd be warm.'

The officers responsible for quartering had simply given each battalion a selected part of the village for billeting. There were none of the usual chalk marks on doors allocating the residence to a set number of men from each company of a particular regiment. Instead, the men simply crammed into the tiny rooms and outhouses. Some properties were boarded up or deserted.

Hallam had wondered if the Dutch had fled first or were kicked out. Small fires lit did not warm the men. There was little talk, and scarcely any liveliness as exhaustion and hunger consumed their thoughts. The battalion's wives looked far worse; numb hands tried to prepare cold foodstuffs, repair their husband's uniforms or look after the children. Even they were subdued.

It was another bitter night. A thin snowfall had stopped and gradually the clouds scudded in the eastern sky to reveal a brightness of cold stars. Hallam, seeking solace, found an inn in a little alley off a wooded park called *Kronenburgerpark* in the centre of the town. The inn was crowded with officers from the other regiments and, despite the day's soul-destroying retreat, were drinking boisterously and laughing in English, German and French.

A pretty serving girl, freckled and smiling, brought Hallam a bottle of wine, a steaming bowl of pease pudding, a plate of cheese and a length of smoked sausage. It was delicious and he ate the food ravenously. He was so famished that he did not notice straight away he had swallowed one of his teeth that had simply come loose from malnourishment.

After finishing the food and drinking the best part of the wine, it became too noisy and a drunken lieutenant with green facings from the 19th roared a huzzah, fell onto Hallam's table and vomited red wine. Hallam stood up, grabbed him by his jacket and threw him onto the floor. One officer laughed at the spectacle and another, possibly a friend, strode towards Hallam to question his intentions. The look on Hallam's face and the dried blood that flecked his unshaven face deterred the officer from seeking violence, and so he crouched to help his friend up.

'We won the day! Cheer up, you morose swine!' shouted another officer. He was red-faced and sweating like a roast hog from the huge hearth fire.

Hallam snarled, but curbed his anger. He paid for his meal and, strode outside where there was a snowman dressed quite accurately as the French General, Charles Pichegru. Someone, possibly the same creator, had also urinated on it. A friendly officer from the Loewenstein regiment stopped him and congratulated him on the battle, offering a cigar. Hallam liked to smoke them now and was grateful for the kindness. They talked a short while and Hallam savoured the smell and taste. Then, the German saw an old friend and Hallam said his farewells, promising if they should ever meet again, they would share a drink and toast fallen friends. Hallam walked back to his lodgings that he unhappily shared with Clements.

He passed a building where rows and rows of wounded soldiers waited for the surgeon. A steady stream of orderlies brought amputated arms and legs wrapped in filthy rags to a growing pile outside. A few men screamed. Most sighed softly or moaned through chapped lips, and some lay still in their torment.

Hallam had been wounded once. A bullet had entered his shoulder and thankfully passed through the flesh not to cause any lasting damage. The surgeon had still probed for fragments of the ball and cloth. The pain of the forceps digging into the wound was worse than the injury itself. He had cursed the surgeon who reeked of rum and sweated and appeared to delight in his agony.

Outside the entrance, he had to step around a puddle of vomit thrown up by another British officer who was lying face-down. He looked up at Hallam, foul yellow liquid dripping from his cheeks, groaned and then retched again. Hallam ignored the man, and went inside. There should have been a small room for Stubbington, but it was empty and Hallam shot the closed door a look of sadness. He climbed the stairs to his quarters when a voice called him from below.

'What is it, Shawford?'

81

The big man held something in his hand. 'I've a present from the wife, sir.'

Hallam descended the steps. 'A present?'

Shawford shuffled awkwardly. 'Yes, sir. For what you did for her and my boy.'

'It was nothing. We all saved them.'

The old soldier shoved the linen wrapped item into his hand. 'God bless you, sir, but you were the one who asked to go back for her. If it wasn't for you...' Shawford's voice trailed away.

Hallam undid the material to find a handsome timepiece. He was shocked at the gift.

'It's not stolen, sir,' Shawford told him upon seeing his expression. 'It's from that Frenchie deserter. I figured he wouldn't be needing it no more and I was going to sell it, but when your own watch was damaged, I spoke to Mrs Shawford and she came up with the idea.'

'I don't know what to say,' Hallam said, touched by the gesture.

Shawford rubbed his hands as though he was suddenly cold. 'A tough fight that.'

'Yes,' Hallam thought of all the dead on the field of Grave. Stubbington, Tipton and he wondered whether Fox and Beckett would survive the surgeon's knife. If they did, he thought, they would face the rest of their lives as crippled beggars, or ruined men destined for the workhouses.

'It felt like we were marching into hell, sir.' Shawford's voice had been hoarse with emotion and Hallam understood that. He had met many old soldiers who would weep at the battles they had endured or of friends lost. The private was a tough man, but sentimental.

'We got burned, but we came through it,' Hallam said, then remembered what Paget had said. 'We'll get home.' He was still dumbfounded by the gift, his eyes gorged on the exquisite timepiece. 'I must give you something towards it, as it must be worth-'

'I won't take a penny, sir,' the private interrupted. 'My wife and boy mean the world to me.'

Hallam outstretched his hand and the private shook it gratefully. 'They are both well?'

'Getting better, sir. Little Jim has a cold, but his shivering has stopped. Rose is as strong as always.'

'That's good.' Hallam thought he ought to enquire of her ordeal, but then decided never to mention it again. 'Merry Christmas to you and your family.'

'You too, sir. Good night.'

When Hallam reached his room, he was surprised to see the fireplace alight with a man warming himself next to a large wide-armed chair. He thought it to be Mr Carew, the regiment's quartermaster.

'Warming your arse again, Tom,' he said, grinning. His boots were loud on the wooden floorboards. 'Sir,' he gasped when he realised that it was actually Colonel Paget.

'Ah, Jack,' Paget replied. 'I hope you don't mind. I had my servant light it for you. Have you eaten?'

'Yes, sir,' Hallam said. 'I haven't written my report of the farmhouse yet. I was going to do that tonight.'

'All in good time.' Paget glanced down at the burgeoning flames that crackled noisily. A moment or two passed by. 'A shame about Stubbington.'

Hallam remembered the boy's cheerfulness and satisfaction at being part of the regiment. 'I'll write a letter to his parents tonight.'

'That's really for your captain to do, Jack,' Paget remarked slightly reprovingly.

'I'll do it, sir,' Hallam said. George Milsum had once told him that it did not do the mind any good to dwell on death, but Hallam remembered the feather swirling around his boots and the guilt of not having more tolerance with the boy snapped at his conscience. 'I want to.'

Paget grunted, knowing that Clements wouldn't bother, or would simply get someone else to do it anyway. 'Very well. Tell them he died a good death.'

Hallam bobbed his head. 'Yes, sir, I will. In time he would have made a fine officer.'

'Agreed.'

The fire crackled loudly. Hallam was puzzled at the colonel's presence. 'Was there something else, sir?'

Paget raised his eyebrows, then clicked his fingers as though he had forgotten. 'Yes, I have something for you,' he said, drawing out two crumpled letters from inside his coat. 'Post.'

'Post?' Hallam frowned.

'The mail, Jack,' Paget replied wryly as he handed them over. 'Five months late I'm afraid, but we're lucky to get any. I have managed to acquire a month old copy of *The Times* waiting for me in my quarters. I'm eager to catch up on the news at home and of course the day reports to sign off, so I won't keep you long.'

Hallam wasn't listening. The first letter was addressed to him and he recognised the lettering. It was from Isabel. His heart quickened with joy. The second letter was addressed to 'Captain Jack Hallam'.

'There's been some mistake,' he said, tearing it open. The paper was thick and creamy, and sealed with a knob of wax that looked as though it had just been stamped. He hurriedly read the letter, which was signed by Paget and dated today. He took a step back in disbelief.

Paget was bemused. 'Are you all right, Captain?' he said with a chuckle.

Hallam looked at him. 'Sir?' he said, then could not find the words and re-read the letter again. Captain. It was something he had always wanted, but it was still a shock. 'What about Captain Clements, sir?' he asked, thinking that he would likely be moved to another company.

'Clements will remain as commander of the company,' Paget said gently. 'It is you that will be transferring out.'

Hallam suddenly felt as though freezing water drenched his heart. 'Sir?'

Paget grimaced as though he had feared Hallam's response. 'You'll be taking over the reins from Captain Vivian who has had his transfer approved.'

'I see,' Hallam hesitated.

Vivian was leaving? So he was being promoted and transferred to Number Seven Company. He felt some of the joy leave because he had worked hard to make the company better. This campaign had toughened them. They were hard men; faces and bodies scarred by violence. Their hair might be unkempt, their coats patched and frayed, and their boots dirtied, but they held their weapons like veterans. And Hallam was proud of them.

Paget saw the expression on his face and must have understood because he spoke gently. 'You've done sterling work, Jack. Don't think I haven't read the reports, or have been blind to your accomplishments in the field and off of it. I see and hear all,' he said, a smile tightening his mouth. 'I am also aware of what kind of an officer you are and have been.'

Hallam had once been put forward for promotion when George Milsum had died, but an altercation with Osborne and his nephew had expunged him from a captaincy. Hallam had caught Osborne's nephew, who was a lieutenant, filching from Milsum's possessions, and Hallam had to be restrained before he had beaten the man senseless. He was let off with a warning, because he was a relation of Osborne's, and who claimed that it was Hallam that started the fight. The damage to his reputation was done and he had remained as a lieutenant until now.

'You are a gallant man,' Paget continued, 'competent, and I need you take your new company under your experienced wing.' His eyes seemed to drink in the dancing flames. 'I am reviewing the status of certain officers in the regiment. I see a new future for the Slashers, and by God I will not tolerate disobedience, negligence and incompetence.' He had been getting angrier as he spoke, but took control of his emotions. He blew out his cheeks. 'There are some who think themselves above the law. For too long, they have been allowed to swagger around like bloody pirates; plundering and marauding. I will not stand for that. The regiment has a proud history; full of heroic deeds and valour. I do not want it remembered for knavish behaviour. I will not have the legend tarnished.'

'I agree, sir,' Hallam replied, nodding his head. This is why he liked Paget. He was young, had his temperaments and his odd ways, but Hallam thought him a kind, wise soul and a damned fine commander.

'Good man. I'm pleased to have you, Jack. I hear the men are already calling you 'Old Steadfast' because of your nerve from the skirmish at the bridge. You've already improved the morale by rescuing Private Shawford's wife and child.' He smiled with approval. 'I'll see you at breakfast at six. We'll only be staying here one night and then we're to march to a place called Arnhem.'

'Well, you know the army, sir - keep on moving even if you aren't going anywhere.'

Paget gave a sardonic smile. 'Quite.' He pulled out a bottle of French brandy and handed it to him. 'Merry Christmas.'

'Thank you, sir,' Hallam said, taking the present. It was a lovely gift and he felt awkward to receive it because he had nothing to give in return. 'Merry Christmas to you too, sir,' he added hurriedly as Paget made for the door.

He waited for the colonel to disappear before putting the brandy on the mantelpiece and opening his wife's letter. He did it carefully because it was precious to him and found it contained two long pages written in her beautiful penmanship.

It was some time later that he emerged from his room. He was so happy that he thought his heart would beat out of his chest. He was still clutching the letter when Clements appeared on the stairs.

'Goddamn Dutch are pleased to see us for once, eh?' Clements, his face flushed red and brow glimmering with sweat, swayed. 'Shame we're pulling out in the morning. Damned fine town. Not the usual hovels and the smell of shit everywhere. There's lots of food and there are some rather attractive women here. Proper breeding. Not the sort that would take a penny to part their legs.' He saw the letter. 'What's that?'

'It's a letter from my wife.' Hallam could smell wine on his breath from a few feet away.

Clements wrinkled his nose at the reply. 'I thought you had orders,' he muttered peevishly. 'It seems to me you're the colonel's favourite at the moment. I thought he might have another special duty for his new pet.' He laughed, pleased with himself.

Hallam did not rise to the mockery. 'No, it's just a letter from home.'

'I never knew you were married.'

'You never bothered to ask,' Hallam said, moving towards the stairs. He was in no mood to speak to Clements. He was going to congratulate Vivian on his transfer before retiring to his room for the night.

Clements scowled 'I don't really care if you're married or not, Lieutenant. In the old days, you had to ask the colonel's permission and even if he agreed, it was frowned upon. Women make men feeble. A feeble man is not fit to be a soldier,' he said, 'even one such as 'Old Steadfast'.' He let out a long lingering laugh that Hallam instantly found irritating.

Hallam looked at him. The captain's shoulders slouched, his coat undone and his waistcoat wet with spilt wine. 'You're drunk,' he grimaced as though talking to him left a bitter taste in his mouth.

'You keep that firebrand tongue still!' Clements spat the last word, whirling a length of spittle onto the floor. 'And so what if I am? What's it to do with you?'

'Drunkenness breeds ill-discipline.'

Clements face went red with ire. 'How dare you-'

Hallam moved away. 'I don't have time for this.'

Clements held up a hand to stop him. 'Your mouth will get you into trouble one day, Lieutenant. Careful you don't disappoint the colonel. Anyway, you don't seem the type to get married. Where did you meet her? Back of some squalid alley? Break her in like some barrack whore, did you?' he said, breaking into another laugh.

Hallam's temper snapped. His right fist struck Clements jaw, and the captain tripped over his steel spurs to topple down the flight of steps. He let out a great bellow of anguish before thudding onto his back at the foot of the stairs, where he lay sprawled, bleeding and groaning.

Hallam casually descended the steps as Paget's adjutant appeared from around the corner of a room he was using as a makeshift briefing room.

'Everything all right?' he said, looking at Clements and then to Hallam.

'You–you hit me,' Clements said disbelievingly, blood showing on his astonished face. His eyes were glassy.

'The captain is three sheets to the wind,' Hallam said.

'I see.'

'He took a tumble down the steps. I'll help him back to his quarters.'

'You hit me!' Clements tried to get up, but swayed.

87

'Would you like a hand, sir?' the adjutant asked Hallam.

'No, thank you. Goodnight.'

The adjutant saw that he wasn't wanted and had far more pressing work to complete so he eagerly went back to his paperwork.

Hallam bent over Clements with a menacing expression.

'You goddamned hit me!' Clements snarled. One of his front teeth was loose, his tongue ran over his split lips. 'You've crossed the line now, Lieutenant! I'll see you broken, and on your knees like your whore!'

'That's Captain Hallam now, you bastard,' Hallam said and stamped on Clements nose, breaking it. Clements howled and whatever he was about to say came out as a gurgle because Hallam kicked him hard in the side of the neck. 'Stubbington was a better officer and a better man than you'll ever be, you drunken piece of shit.' Hallam took hold of his ankles and dragged Clements back up the stairs where his head hitting every step with a thud. One of the spurs came loose and clinked as it tumbled away. At the top of the stairs, Hallam pushed open the door to an unoccupied room and unceremoniously dumped the unconscious captain onto the floor. He closed the door and turned the key in the lock.

He returned downstairs to find Vivian to congratulate him, and then retired to his room as the church bells rang. He gazed out of the window. The stars were so bright it was as though you could reach up and snuff them out, he thought. It was Christmas Day and it was snowing again, but Hallam didn't care. Pulling off his boots and socks, he sat down on the chair next to the still blazing fire. The chair was upholstered, tatty and much worn about the arms, but it was exceedingly comfortable. He moved the logs with the iron and the wood crackled and spat. He wiggled his toes on the aged hearth-fire rug, feeling the luxurious heat seep into his chilled bones, yet, rubbed his hands that were thrumming with the pain of cold flesh warming.

Remembering something in his pocket, he pulled out the blue feather, gazing at it for a moment pensively before putting it on the mantelpiece where two beeswax candles guttered from the draughty floorboards. He would send it with the letter to Stubbington's parents.

He sat back in the chair, sagging slightly, and unfolded Isabel's letter again and smiled.

It was dated 25th May, and she wrote that she was two months pregnant.

The baby must be due any day now and Hallam could already be a father, and the feeling was so wonderful that tears pricked at his eyes. If it was a boy, he would name him William after his father.

The sound of singing outside the room echoed up along the street. German voices and they were singing carols. It was Christmas and he was a captain and a father. A father!

He took a swig of the brandy, eyes glistening in the firelight.

It was a magical Christmas.

HISTORICAL NOTE

The Flanders Campaign of 1793-1795 was conducted during the first years of the French Revolutionary War by the allied states of the First Coalition and the French First Republic. The allied aim was to invade France by mobilising its armies along the French frontiers to bully it into submission.

In the north, the allies' immediate aim was to expel the French from the Dutch Republic and the Austrian Netherlands, then march directly to Paris. Britain invested a million pounds to finance their Austrian and Prussian allies. Twenty thousand British troops under George III's younger son, Prince Frederick, the Duke of York, were eventually tied up in the campaign.

Austrian Prince Josias of Saxe-Coburg was in overall command, but answered directly to Emperor Francis II, while the Duke of York was given objectives set by William Pitt the Younger's Foreign Minister, Henry Dundas. Thus, from the outset, mixed political machinations and ignorance hindered the operation.

The French armies on the other-hand also suffered. Many from the old royalist officer class had emigrated following the revolution, which left the cavalry severely undermanned and those officers that remained were fearful of being watched by the representatives. The price of failure or disloyalty was the guillotine. After the Battle of Hondshoote, September 1793, the British and Hanoverians under the Duke of York were defeated by General Houchard and General Jourdan. Houchard was arrested for treason for failing to organise a pursuit and guillotined.

By the spring of 1793, the French had virtually marched into the Dutch Republic and Austrian Netherlands unopposed. In May, the British won a victory at Famars and then followed up the success for the siege of Valenciennes. However, instead of concentrating, the allies dispersed their forces in an attempt to mop up the scattered French outposts. The French re-organised and combined their troops. Dundas requested the Duke of York to lay siege to Dunkirk who had to abandon it after a severe mauling at Hondshoote.

By the end of the year the allied forces were now stretched. The Duke of York, unable to offer support the Austrians and Prussians, because the army was suffering from supply problems and by Dundas who was withdrawing regiments in order to re-assign them to the West Indies.

The French counter-offensive in the spring of the following year smashed apart the fragile allied lines. The Austrian command broke down as Francis II called for a withdrawal. At the Battle of Feurus, the defeated Austrians; abandoning their century long hold of the Netherlands, retreated north towards Brussels. The loss of the Austrian support and the Prussians (who had also fallen back) led to the campaign's collapse.

The French advanced unchecked.

By the autumn The Duke of York had been replaced by Sir William Harcourt, but with rumoured peace talks, the British position looked increasingly vulnerable. The only allied success of that year was that of the 'Glorious First of June', when Britain's Lord Howe defeated a French naval squadron in the Atlantic, sinking one and capturing six French ships.

The winter of 1794 was one of the worst any one had ever imagined. Rivers froze, men died in the sleep, disease was rampant, and the soldier's uniforms fell apart. It was an extremely harsh winter, because the army was starving due to the collapsed commissariat. Troops started to steal from the local inhabitants. The officers were too lazy or indifferent to control them, and discipline amongst some units broke down completely.

By the spring of 1795, the British reached the Hanoverian port of Bremen. They arrived back in Britain, weak, ill and emaciated. Some never fully recovered.

The Flanders Campaign demonstrated a series of weaknesses of the British Army. The Duke of York was given the role as Commander-in-Chief and brought forth a programme of reform. It created the professional army that was to fight with much success throughout the Peninsular War.

The allies abandoned the Low Countries. Britain did attempt to undertake a second invasion of the newly proclaimed Batavian

Republic in 1799 under The Duke of York, but it faltered and proved disastrous.

Notoriously, a children's rhyme about the Holland campaign mocked the leadership of the Duke of York:

Oh, The grand old Duke of York,
He had ten thousand men;
He marched them up to the top of the hill,
And he marched them down again.

And when they were up, they were up,
And when they were down, they were down,
And when they were only half-way up,
They were neither up nor down

However, there is another satirical verse attributed to Richard Tarlton, and so was adapted where possible, the latest being The Duke of York. The oldest version of the song dates from 1642:

The King of France with forty thousand men,
came up the hill and so came downe againe

Many officers who would continue to serve their countries received their baptism of fire on the fields of Flanders. Arthur Wesley, the future Duke of Wellington, was colonel of the 33rd Foot and saw his first action at the Battle of Boxtel. The Austrian Archduke Charles fought in Flanders, as did several of Napoleon's marshals: Jourdan, Ney, Murat, Mortier and Bernadotte. The Prussian General Sharnhorst, another great reformer of the Napoleonic Wars, saw battle under the Duke of York.

Lieutenant Jack Hallam of the 28th North Gloucestershire Regiment of Foot is sadly an invention, as are most of the characters mentioned in this novella, except Lieutenant-Colonel Edward Paget who did command The Slashers. The regiment were part of the British 6th Brigade, and were active throughout the campaign; fighting rear-guard actions amid the retreat. Grave, a Dutch fortified town, was besieged by three thousand French during December. The

Dutch garrison surrendered by the end of 1794. The battle depicted in this novella is based on the skirmish at Tiel, where an allied contingent under General Dundas drove the French back south of the frozen River Waal. The allies could not hold the town due to an overwhelming French force, and so had to retreat past Arnhem and across the Rhine.

The Flanders Campaign may have ended in failure, but the 28th was one of the regiments that remained unwavering and dependable. Lord Cathcart wrote in his General Orders, *"Whenever danger is to be apprehended and difficulties to be surmounted, you have the 27th and the 28th to call upon"*.

The 28th returned home in May 1795, and later embarked for the West Indies. A gale known as 'Admiral Christian's Storm' sprang up when the convoy was at sea and four companies of the battalion made it safely to Barbados to assist in the capture of St Lucia in 1796. The other six companies returned home and were sent to garrison Gibraltar. The complete regiment went on to Malta and sailed with Sir Ralph Abercromby's Expeditionary Army to Egypt.

I am indebted to several people. Lady Elizabeth Longford's *Wellington: The Years of the Sword*, and Professor Richard Holmes' *Wellington: The Iron Duke*, helped me to see the campaign through the eyes of the great man. Holmes also wrote the truly wonderful *Redcoat: The British Soldier in the Age of Horse and Musket*. This is an excellent and comprehensive study of the British Army, which I found invaluable. For anyone wanting to read more about the campaign, I recommend reading Christopher Hibbert's *The French Revolution*.

I must thank Jacqui Reiter for her beta-reading, Catherine Lenderi, who really helped fine tune this story, and Jenny Quinlan who brought the jacket cover to life with her talent for design.

Jack Hallam has more adventures to come.

9640965R00054

Printed in Great Britain
by Amazon.co.uk, Ltd.,
Marston Gate.